Wind River Winter

Wind River Winter

VIRGINIA STEM OWENS

ZONDERVAN PUBLISHING HOUSE • GRAND RAPIDS, MICHIGAN

A JUDITH MARKHAM BOOK

WIND RIVER WINTER
Copyright © 1987 by Virginia Stem Owens

Judith Markham Books are published by
the Zondervan Publishing House
1415 Lake Drive, S.E., Grand Rapids, Michigan 49506

Library of Congress Cataloging in Publication Data
Owens, Virginia Stem.
  Wind River winter.

  1. Death—Religious aspects—Christianity. 2. Owens,
Virginia Stem. I. Title.
BT825.094 1987   236'.1   87-6172
ISBN 0-310-45861-7

Printed in the United States of America

87 88 89 90 91 / CH / 10 9 8 7 6 5 4 3 2 1

To David

Another self seemed to arise, like a white spirit from a dead man, from the dumb and trampled self of the past. Doubtless, this self must again die and be buried, and again from its tomb, spring a winged child; but of this my history as yet bears not the record. Self will come to life even in the slaying of self; but there is ever something deeper and stronger than it, which will emerge at last from the unknown abysses of the soul: will it be with a solemn gloom, burning with eyes? or a clear morning after the rain? or a smiling child, that finds itself nowhere, and everywhere?

George Macdonald, *Phantastes*

CONTENTS

Prologue

One day last year in the middle of June I was descending a
trail leading from the lip of a rocky Wyoming ridge down to
the sagebrush flats in the canyon below. Suddenly a hawk
dropped through the branches of the pines in a lazy,
controlled parabola and, hanging at the nadir of its long arc
for a moment, grasped a negligent picketpin in its claw and
flew away among the trees again.

I stood in the thicket of limberpine for a good quarter
of an hour wondering about the secluded morality play I
had stumbled into. It had been played out with a certain
ease and grace and matter-of-factness. The small rodent had
not squealed or struggled. The only sound had been the
sheerest shuffle of wind through the bird's wings. It caused
no more stir on the rocky slope than my sitting down to
breakfast did in my house.

So this was death—from natural causes, as we say.
Death descending from the sky on silent wings. Death with
implacable, immobilizing talons that somewhere, not far from
me, were ripping open the small warm carcass while I still
stood under the tree. The necessary death of this world.
Death destroying for the sake of life.

I went on down the trail, maneuvering the switchbacks and trying to keep my analogies under control. For I sometimes thought I heard wings overhead myself.

There is a dove in heaven, we know, that descends when the skies open, sometimes in fire. But perhaps there is also a hawk in heaven that swoops down on us with the gift of death to deliver us from our used-up past, the past we have neither the courage nor the imagination to walk away from.

If, like a figure in a medieval painting, I could have appeared not only where I was conscious of being from moment to moment there along the exposed face of a rockslide, but also simultaneously at points higher up and lower down the trail, if I could have turned back and observed my own descent, what would I have seen? A figure frowning slightly, someone absorbed, in a way the picketpin never knew, in the disintegration of the pattern of her life.

My mother had had a tumor removed. My grandfather was losing his memory. My husband's vocation was hanging

in suspension. In a month's time I would be moving I
didn't know where yet. My daughters would stay behind,
committed now to their own plans. The matrix of
circumstances that contained my life was coming apart, not
cleanly, but in jagged, splintered ends. Death was in the air
over my head. The end of a way of living that would never
come again. If I lived through the year to another June, it
would only be because I had done a good job of dying in
the coming winter.

I intended to stay in this Wyoming wilderness over the
winter, for it is an instructive place to learn about death,
even to learn how to die. Here, death is not covered over or
whisked out of sight. In the wilderness things die in the
open. In fact, when winter descends on the northern Rockies
and grips the land with its obdurate talons, death becomes
the daily diet of contemplation. Animal populations are
thinned of their weak members. Vegetation sinks its capital
into its deepest roots. And the wind scours even the stones
of any detritus of extraneous life.

Not many people want to contemplate death. We live in
terrified times, and our world is understandably more
interested in images of reassurance and rebirth than it is in
death. At each moment, death that could be the end of
history waits to erupt from the Wyoming underground
weapons silos, let loose by some hand over which we have
no control. Children grow up not just under the shadow of
their own deaths and the deaths of those they love, but
under the shadow of world-death, future-death.

Perhaps our fear of death at others' hands is so great
that we cannot concentrate on our own task of dying. We
ignore that discipline and attempt to be born again without
dying first.

If so, I don't know that we are so very different from
other ages. There have, in fact, been spaces in history when
whole civilizations have been driven mad with death. In
fourteenth-century Europe and the Aztec empire, for
example, populations wallowed in death to inure themselves
to its terrors. Perhaps this is our own motive for watching
people being killed over and over, artificially and not very
accurately, on television. Perhaps this is our unconscious
Aztecan ritual that accustoms us to the terror of death.

But we are not the first generation to live in a reign of

terror, despite television and our technological weapons.
Apocalypse has threatened—and happened—before. The
world, as its inhabitants then knew it, has been destroyed
before. Sodom and Gomorrah incinerated and smoking on
the plains is only a scale model for our own fears about the
future. The citizens of those cities knew not much more of
the world than their own neighborhood. To them the fire
and brimstone were, effectually, the end of the world.
Holocaust is not new among humankind. Jericho, Jerusalem,
Rome, Dresden, Hiroshima, Hué—all the world that
somebody knew has gone up in flames before.

This is the death that is the enemy, the death that aims
at the unmaking of creation. This is the enemy that desires
creation's diminution, its degradation. This is the death that
would destroy the world if it could, either in one great
conflagration or by sucking life slowly at whatever fissure it
finds in our cells or our souls.

But if death is *only* the enemy, how then do we dare
speak of the necessity of death in our lives, of how we must
die with Christ, be in fact baptized into his death? Why
does the common table at the heart of our faith commemo-
rate the very death of our Savior? Do we celebrate life or
death when we consume body and blood?

And what, after all, is the nature of this death? Is it
indeed the necessarily opposing force to life that holds
reality together as pictured in the light and dark of the yin-
yang symbol? Is it only a part of the cyclical process of
being? Do we protest against it only because our flesh,
entangled in time, deludes us? Is death actually a release
from the illusions of time and space and particularity? Is it
rest? A sleep and a forgetting? Or is it punishment? The
wages of sin? Should we desire it, as Paul did, as access to
the presence of God? Or should we cry out against the
dying of the light?

Certainly there is the death that, within the context of
earthly existence, is necessary. If all beings were on earth
immortal, where would food come from? Or time, for that
matter? We know little enough about this kind of death and
do not contemplate it sufficiently to understand our own
creaturely nature.

And what is the meaning of that great lost word of the
church, one it seldom utters now—our death in Christ? Why

are we called upon to embrace this enemy? Why did not
Jesus, like his Jewish kin, the Maccabees and the Essenes,
build a fortress against the enemy where we could all
huddle together in safety? Why did he, to "deliver them
who through fear of death were all their lifetime subject to
bondage," invade the kingdom of death itself? Why did he
seek out death, that place becalmed, transfixed, immobile?
Why didn't the light ignore the darkness? Why did it have
to enter it, confront it on that frontier between consciousness
and chaos?

We forget that we too are called to that place. We too
find life only by losing it. To know the power of the
Resurrection, Paul, who had already had his share of killing,
said that he must share Christ's suffering, "becoming like
him in his death." We too must learn to lay down our lives
and walk away from them.

No death therapy can help us here. Breaking the process
of dying down by analysis into five or any other number of
stages is insufficient to our needs. We play parlor games
with the psyche to subdue reality. That may be entirely
necessary. Even Aristotle described Greek drama as a useful
tool for coping. But coping isn't always what's called for,
especially if it's a defense against life.

I believe all life to come from God. I also know that
the approach to the source of that life lies only through the
valley of the shadow of death, our death in Christ. Death is
that narrow, straight gate through which we struggle toward
the light. There is no other way, and that way is so lean, so
constricted, that it scrapes all the flesh from our skeletal
selves before we can writhe and heave through the aperture.
Whoever enters there leaves everything behind: brothers,
sisters, mother and father, home, hope, fear, fancy. All the
flesh is scraped off in that centrifugal force, the bones
tumbled smooth as stones.

Annie Dillard asks, "Did you think before you were
caught, that you needed, say, life? Do you think you will
keep your life, or anything else you love? But no. Your
needs are all met. But not as the world giveth. . . . You see
the creatures die, and you know that you will die. And one
day it occurs to you that you must not need life." And
Bonhoeffer, amid quite different circumstances and with the
heightened awareness that war with this world brings, put

the case more succinctly: "When Christ calls a man he bids him come and die."

For human beings, the necessary death, the death essential to life, is always voluntary, which is what makes it so hard. The rest of creation, though it dies, is spared the need to make an act of the will. Death simply comes upon it and overshadows it, in the dive of the osprey, the pounce of the coyote, the freezing of cells. Our own bodies, thanks be to God, share this much with creation.

Nevertheless, in everything but will, creation—dumb, brute creation—can show us something of how even this voluntary dying is done. Indeed, how else can we know death except among the creatures?

I watched a fellow creature dying this summer, a friend. Even though cancer had been grinding away on his body for several years, there was still so much sheer health left in him that he was having a hard time dying. A thin, hot thread pulsed through his veins. His fine-grained skin was flushed and damp. Despite the age and dereliction of his body, little white whiskers were still growing on his cheeks. Only the eyes were cloudy. Not much muscle or flesh was left on him, but what was there was still of exceptionally fine quality. All that health had to *go* somewhere before he could die. There seemed to be a thin tube out of which life could leave him, and it was bottlenecked from the pressure of the remaining health.

He slept for about four seconds at a time and then came to for about the same length of time. His mouth, the salivary glands having been removed, had to be almost constantly irrigated with a medicine dropper. When I dribbled too much water into his mouth, he coughed and almost sounded normal, the tiny gestures of recovering from the cough almost looking natural, even though he had been in a coma for days.

It was like watching a canyon erode. A little more substance washed away each hour, and then he "stabilized," the way a riverbank stabilizes. Then there was another rush, more pressure from the disease, and the body gave way a bit more. But it was a slow, almost imperceptible process. The wear showed more on the soft tissue of the healthy watchers than on him who was worn down to the bedrock. It was, in fact, days more before the last thin layer crumbled.

I learned something about death, sitting by the bedside that afternoon, acquired an icon I could study for a glimmer of what I am called to. But such occasions are rare.

Even our ties to earth-death are being systematically cut off. We neither kill nor harvest the food for our own tables. It comes to us already death-processed. We have no bone-deep knowledge that other things die so that we may eat and live. How then can we possibly sense the depth of sacrifice that atonement requires? Our salvation seems easy and grace cheap because we have lost the death link to our tables. Since we are deprived of death within our own dwellings, we must look elsewhere for instructive examples. Outside.

Outside, the world itself dies every year. We have almost forgotten that. The sun withdraws its light, the darkness overshadows the earth. The waters freeze and the leaves decay. We forget because we don't have to live in that world anymore. We have created our own world where we have as much light and heat as we desire—hot, running water, and strawberries the year round. We exempt ourselves from the season of death that envelops the world outside our artificial environment. We live as though on an alien planet; this has become our imitation victory over death.

One has to go all the way to the wilderness to really be outside now. To do my necessary dying, I would come back to this place in the Wind River Mountains where the world still dies so thoroughly and with such skill. If nothing else, I could learn the length of dying, its own capacious stretch through time and space. For death takes its own sweet time. It refuses to be rushed. I needed an apprenticeship, the daily practice, the careful observation of the pace of dying. Going to bed and getting up with winter, day in, day out. Grappling with cold, finding connections between the exchanges of energy we call death. Watching life abandon the land, observing the dereliction of creation.

And maybe those mute lessons would seep slowly into the landscape of my own mind, so that I could learn to bear the abandonment of my own life. Maybe, watching the world die, I could learn to enter into that absolute still center at the heart of the universe, the death of Christ, where I could leave everything behind.

September

When I come back to the Wind River Mountains in
September, they are different than they were in June.
Clouds of dust boil up behind the car on the road up the
canyon. The sparse prairie grass, each individual blade a
thin, visible stroke against the dun background of the
hillsides, was tenderly green in early June. Now the horses
have cropped it close for three months and every trail looks
like hammered aluminum from their hoof prints. What green
is left on the slopes is neither tender nor fresh. It is the
gray-green of olive leaves, of vegetation that survives with
little water and lots of dust.

My husband and I will spend the winter alone up this
canyon that snakes between a high lateral moraine and cliffs
cut into the mountain by a glacier. In the canyon's palm are
cupped three lakes: Torrey, Ring, and Trail. A creek that
comes pouring down from the very backbone of the
continent runs through the lakes and finally empties into the
Wind River as it reaches the highway. Our cabin, six miles
up the canyon, sits between the two farthest lakes—Trail
and Ring. There the creek makes a bend and ambles

sideways across the canyon floor before straightening again and debouching into Ring Lake. Our front window faces northwest, toward the Absoraka Range and Togwotee Pass, the eastern approach to the Tetons.

September is the month the sagebrush comes into its glory. By nature it is barely green, paler even than olive trees. It makes only the feeblest gesture toward verdancy, hoarding its powers for sheer survival, not squandering them on vain appearances. It is only now, after all the other plants have long ago blossomed and their blooms dried and dropped, that the sagebrush, most cautious of plants, finally puts forth its flowers. Not in spring, but in autumn.

We walk everywhere held in a golden nimbus of sagebrush pollen. It settles in our hair, on the lips, in the creases of our clothes, like spray-borne salt at the seashore. The long spikes of flowers, in fact, only look yellow because of the pollen, not the petals. They are otherwise scarcely flowers at all, the sort called "inconspicuous" by the field guides. Even upon close examination, all that is visible of their inflorescence are the stamen and pistils, thick with a yellow, fecund dust like the golden pollen that showered down on Danaë as a disguise for the lustful Zeus.

Dust thou art. Life in the arid lands is always dust. Not only in death, but even in fertility, in the act of life-passing.

The dun-colored hills and the gray-green sagebrush with their ochre out-of-season flowers are relieved by the evergreens, the pines, juniper, fir, and spruce. They will be dark green all winter, standing against the bare hills, the rocks, the snow. The conifers drop their leaves discreetly, at the backs of the branches where the loss doesn't show. The needles fall around their feet in shining accumulations, a copper-colored coverlet. Beneath this top layer the needles have already begun to decay and turn to black powdery humus—mold, real soil, meager and difficult to find in this rocky country. The needles fall and feed, eventually, the roots. A fortunate arrangement where there is so little food. It would be as though you and I could subsist on our hair and nail parings and dried flecks of flesh. And much, much light.

I come here to the Wind River Mountains for the winter with David, my husband, who, like me, like all of us, is dying. Ten years after his ordination, his vocation is shriveling and drying. And there is no guarantee that, come spring, any new growth will appear. "What will I be when this winter is over?" he wonders aloud.

Neither of us knows what waits at the end of this dark tunnel we're entering, what we will be when the winter is over, or where we will go. All we can see are the first signs of the retreat of life. The yellow on the cottonwoods. The bunch grass sinking its tough fortunes into its roots, going underground where it can hide from the coming winter.

Only the sagebrush, putting forth its untimely pollen, seems certain of another spring.

How many times do we have to die in this life, get worn down to nothing? Everything is constantly rubbing against something else. The wind scours the stony-hearted mountains. The cornhusks from last night's supper grate against the gut wall. The hawk's wings flail the air over the lake. The river runs over the stones it has already shaved smooth with centuries of liquid friction. The chainsaw blade rips through the tree, its racket battering against our ear drums. And our very breath pushes and scrubs the walls of the lungs. With all this constant erosion, it's a wonder there's anything left at all except a little pile of dust and a puff of air to blow it about. It says something for substance that the world wears so well.

When something dies, it does not simply disappear. That's a false notion of death that we, sheltered as we are by the commercial disposal of corpses, have deluded ourselves with. A dead body is still a body. It still has substance and lies there, taking up space, filling the view. The leaves do not simply evaporate from the trees or evanesce into the air. They fall to the ground and only gradually get eaten by bacteria, mixed with the soil, flattened and blackened by rain and snow, and so wear away to earth after several seasons.

Translation, on the other hand, may be instantaneous. The chariot that swung low for Elijah whisked him abruptly away. Even resurrection for all I know may well occur "in a moment, in the twinkling of an eye." But death is long. Dying is at length. It takes the world several months to die every year.

I had a friend once who, inspired by the Epistle to the Philippians, decided to practice dying as a spiritual exercise. He would come home from work, worn out and fretted by a job he didn't like, to a house with crying babies and a restless wife, and he would lay down and die. Prostrate himself on the floor in the midst of domestic detritus and play dead, like a possum. He would fold his hands across his chest, close his eyes, and pretend it was all over. All the toil and strain to make a living, to make a life. No more obligations. No more responsibilities. No more opportunity to make his mark on an already crosshatched and scored world.

He said he found it marvelously soothing, playing possum. Just the promise of death, just a foretaste, was enough to calm his frazzled nerves. But it demanded discipline. In fact, after about a week he lost the hang of it. He could no longer die effectively. Life crept in again with its demands for decisions, its aggravating action. He only speaks longingly now of how he used to be able to die.

I don't know if he needed more practice, more years, what. I admit it's hard to die with a two-year-old crawling across your corpse. At first the babies think it's a new game. They try to pry your eyes open, stick a finger in your

mouth, pull your ears. Then, getting no response, they begin
to whimper and cry. And they cry so cunningly, it's difficult
to deny their demands that you live. So you raise up on an
elbow, pop your eyes open, and say Boo! to reassure them
that it was only a game you were playing. And there goes
your little bit of death for the day.

We two, of course, no longer have those distractions.
What were once our two-year-olds are now miles away, busy
living a life without our help. We can get on with it, this
practiced stillness, this nonintervention policy we have
negotiated with the world. We can suck in our sap from our
extremities and shove it down, down into the roots to wait
out the winter. We can let the crisped, dry leaves and
blades fall or get beaten off by the weather. There is no
one to pry open our eyes, stick a plump finger in our
mouths, no one to demand that we live.

The first snow of the season has come upon us
suddenly, sooner than we had expected. Yesterday, Sunday
morning, was gray and shrouded. By midafternoon a cold
rain mixed with sleet had begun to fall. Then, briefly, the
sun came out to set, lighting up the wet leaves and grass. A
chunk of rainbow appeared to the northeast. Scraps of clouds
floated down the canyon under the innocent blue sky. We
thought the storm was over. One of those short notices
winter sends ahead to let you know it's coming.

We woke this morning to a sky not gray this time but
white. In the night I had heard the sleet hitting the window
like tiny teeth biting at the glass. But this morning the sleet
had changed to snow. Snow is silent; it does not chitter at
the windows but falls noiselessly, which is why it always
surprises.

It will not last, of course. By nine o'clock the
thermometer already shows one degree above freezing. But
still the snow falls, filling in the ground between the
sagebrush and the boulders with white, covering the dun
ground. No one expected this much. And so early, everyone
agrees.

Later I sit by the window in the second cabin, the one
I use for a study, the fire just catching in the stove behind
me but the room not yet heated. I look out at the snow still
falling on the other side of the creek. The cliffs make the

snow visible high up in the air. It moves in currents, like a grainy river running overhead, as the wind carries it down the canyon. The fir trees, the pine and alders along the creek bank, washed clean of dust now, gleam with dark and various greens. A ground squirrel skitters from under a currant bush up onto a rock and back again. A robin, ignoring the weather, flies in to scout the bare ground under the brush.

The snow makes a stark white page for all this busy life to write upon. When the ground is bare, its dun color absorbs everything in camouflage. Nothing stands out. Even the evergreens are diminished. But with snow! All particulars spring out. Details are distinct. The fence posts, white on one side, wetly black on the other. The rocks, iced like cake. The trees, every bole and branch discernible even through the green boughs. Contrast. Hard edges. Clear definition. Black, perfect calligraphy on a cold, white page.

To read this word written on the white world, you must become oblivious to storms yourself. This particular hieroglyph for "beautiful" has a price. It is not come by easily. No one, of course, insists you buy. The world is not hawking its wares the way it does in the spring. Stay inside by the fire. It doesn't care. It will keep this word to itself as readily as not, hidden from stove-warmed hearts and feet.

It continued to snow steadily all through the day and night. In fact it is still snowing now at midmorning, although the flakes are finer and do not fall so thick. We may not know all the sixty varieties of snow that Eskimos can name, but living in the mountains, one learns at least several kinds. The sort that is falling now is unusual in our canyon. Its large flakes are weighted with moisture. Hardly any wind has come with it either, which is why it has piled up to the unusual depth of about two feet this morning.

Around four o'clock yesterday afternoon the temperature finally dropped below freezing and the snow started to stick. I went out to have a look around and gather some flowers and twigs to decorate the cabin for our housewarming party. I stumbled across great black holes in the snow, the entrances to burrows, damply dark against the white. But there were no animal tracks at all. Whatever was out there was sitting tight. The alders and cottonwood down by the water were weighted over with the heavy wet snow caught in the still-green leaves. It is, after all, still officially summer by the calendar. Fall doesn't even start for a week yet.

In the meadow the yellow chamisa and the goldenrod, the blue mountain gentians, still blooming, were already covered with snow. But near the road I found gumweed, its yellow rays made even more brilliant by the ice crystals that clogged the leaves. Red rosehips sprang out from the briary bushes where their leaves were caked with ice.

At the water gap where the horses come down to drink in summer, ice was clotted on the long tail hairs caught in the barbed wire.

I grabbed some gumweed, a few rosehips and pine cones, some boughs of juniper and fir to put in a basket with a stalk of magenta sorrel seeds. That was all. Everything else was covered with snow already.

That night friends, who live nearby in summer but who will be going away soon, packed into a rickety Land Rover and came down the hill. It was already dark when they came and the snow still fell thick. Our cabin, with the lights burning, the stove going, the food hot, was like a glowing coal in a dying fire.

A few days ago I was thinking about my winter's work, the spiritual discipline of dying. Such a discipline is the necessarily unremitting struggle to crack the sides of the old self in order to become in actuality what only potentially existed before. To grow up into the full—or even the partial—stature of Christ requires a series of deaths. And once the birth-death process starts, there's no going back. There are moments when, caught in the contracting birth canal, I want there to be some other way. I have the familiar yearning to be re-made, suddenly and effortlessly, as though touched by a magic wand. I would prefer magical transformation to dying, I thought.

But hard on the heels of such a thought, so hard in fact as to have the force of a direct word, came the sudden and terrible knowledge of what granting such a wish could mean: To be magically transformed would mean the obliteration of my own created being to make a place for somebody else, someone who is not me. I felt, physically felt, the hiatus in time and the rupture in the continuity of

the cosmos this would make. A fissure would open in
physical reality into which the self—that accumulation of
engrammed experiences and chemical structures we call the
personality—would disappear, not just to become invisible,
but to cease to be. Like that moment when the frog in the
cartoon frame goes—pop—and disappears just before he
turns into a prince. Unless one wants to be entirely unmade,
to go spinning off into the primordial chaos, to end up on
the cosmic compost heap, one had better decide to cooperate
with grace.

There is nothing easy about grace, nor even pleasant.
Indeed the magic-wand method seems a good deal easier.
But then *I* would never be around to appreciate and enjoy
that easiness because *I* would no longer exist. Instead, there
would be someone else in my place, someone with no
appreciation for the trials she had missed. An imposter.
Neither the unmade self nor the imposter would have
profited by the disjunctive "pop" or the piggyback jump
over the abyss.

Magic wands to get us over the hard parts are not the
same as death and resurrection. If I want the self-I-am
brought to fruition, it must be squeezed and scraped through
the narrow birth-gate of our obedience that includes dying.
Death and unmaking are not the same experience.
Unmaking, in fact, is not an experience at all.

Still, my weakness is such that at times I would prefer
even that—obliteration—to the hard dying I am called to. I
am a coward. I can only force myself through the hard parts
by considering these alternatives.

Today the snow is sinking. The ground beneath it is
still warm enough to undermine its lowest level, turning it
to liquid.

A rabbit comes and sits at the window, looking in at us
for the better part of an hour. It is a very Durer-like rabbit,
a cottontail, smaller-bodied than domestic breeds. It pulls its
head down into its shoulders. The eyes are large and dark,
and it turns its head sideways to see us better. It sits, its
front toes turned slightly inward, and stares solemnly. Ever
so often it wiggles its nose and shifts back and forth on its
feet.

Today the thermometer goes up above 40° and there is

intermittent sunshine. We wade through a sherbet surf halfway to our knees, looking for tracks. The rabbits' tracks, both abults' and babies', are everywhere. They head down from the cabin or nearby burrows to the creek. The pattern of mouse feet print the snow like alternate leaves on a stem. They only loop out a short way from the shelter of sagebrush cover and back again. Sometimes we find an abrasion in the snow around the tracks where they stop abruptly. Some hunting hawk or owl has swooped down out of the sky, beating the snow with its wings while it gripped the mouse.

Further out on the flat away from the creek there are scarcely any tracks at all. But closer to the rocks that rise in ridges behind us, we begin to pick up more tracks again. The rocks provide a certain amount of cover for small creatures. They also provide vantage points for the predators. We find the paw print of a cat there, and the less concealed, long, loping stride of a coyote, showing where he climbed the ridge to howl into the storm.

We find no tracks of larger animals, no deer or elk. Nor will we until the hunting season has passed and they feel out the safety of the canyon and the willow-rich creek bottom again.

The storm has won at least one round. A hunter died this week in the Big Horn Mountains from exposure. A father and son were hunting together. The father broke his leg, and the son tried to hike out of the mountains for help, leaving his father behind in the tent. The son was found three days later in deep snow. They were only eight miles from town.

As we hiked up the road this morning we spotted a coyote loping diagonally up a ridge above us. At the top it turned and stood for a moment, changing to gold in the moist morning light. Coyotes, in most lights, are not gold but that mottled combination of dun and gray that covers most wild creatures here. Technically, they are called cryptic. Hidden. Camouflaged by their coloration that echoes the earth they grow on. But this one, for a moment, owing to the peculiar slant of sun and his vantage above us, showed gold.

There is a bounty on the heads of these dogs, and an old-timer has already predicted a lot of pelts will be brought in this winter with so many of the miners, loggers, and oil-field roughnecks out of work.

This morning, the first without a cloud since the storm, we ride up to the far ridge on horseback with a friend. The horses take us easily to the top of the spine from which the ribs of two valleys fall away—Torrey Creek on one side and Wind River on the other. On the southern side the early snow is almost gone, except for where it is packed under densely branched trees. But on the northern side, separated by only a foot or so of spinal column, several inches still lie, crystallized and hard.

The austere Absorakas are clear, their many-canyoned badlands striated into layers of mauve, pink, red, gray, green. We turn to the southwest and there, incredibly close, are the snowfields topping the Wind River peaks of Arrow, Circle, and Whiskey mountains. Our snow may have melted, inconsequential and transient, but the snow on those peaks will likely be there till spring.

Down below, dropped at our feet in this glacial valley scoured out by boulders, lie the lakes—Trail, Ring, and Torrey—in a line that loops along the valley floor. Ring Lake glistens in today's sun like an abalone shell, the various algae in its waters showing purple and blue and green. From this height the cabins alongside the lakes are tinier than Monopoly counters.

We take an inventory of the topography, naming over the peaks from east to west, just as we always do—as though an entire mountain might have disappeared since the last time we were up on the ridge.

The Old Testament lesson in church today rang out like a warning not to contract too closely with winter. *But the godless call with deed and word for Death, counting him friend, they wear themselves out for him, with him they make a pact, and are fit to be his partners.*

We lurch to our knees for prayers, stand up to sing, finally collapse in the pew for the sermon. We are on unfamiliar turf in this little log church dedicated to St. Thomas the Doubter and have to keep a sharp eye out for the proper posture. They take the etymology of "liturgy"—

the people's work—seriously. They don't let you loll about on the pews.

At the communion rail we hold our hands cupped like children accepting a surprise. The wafer, pale and thin as a fingernail paring, sticks to the roof of my mouth. I prod it loose with my tongue. Then the wine comes round, the cup of salvation, its garnet contents tipped gingerly into my mouth. One would like to stay there till the dehydrated dough had a chance to dissolve and slide down the throat, but there are others pushing up behind for their turn at the bread of life.

In the afternoon David goes fishing on Trail Lake in the canoe. Behind him the sun makes a bridge of light on the wind-lapped water. He and the canoe are a black silhouette against this backdrop of crushed gold foil.

A cat's track on the lake path. How does it manage to leave only one clear impression on the ground, as though it flew, touching down only occasionally?

Also, a Clark's nutcracker, most fractious of birds, hangs head down to strip a pine cone of its kernels. It's flustered when I catch it in such an unguarded position, and makes a raucous flap, cursing me in bird oaths.

The hideout of the merganser ducks is in a little cove on the far side of the lake. It is so marshy and tangled with brush there that they don't expect company, and I am able to slip up quite close before they sense a foreign presence and paddle farther out into the lake.

All this on an afternoon's walk that dips and rises slightly over the roots of the moraine that shores up the lake. I have the pockets of my jacket panniered with a pint-size thermos cup on one side and a book on the other. The crevices are filled in with lip balm and pens, reading glasses, and handkerchiefs. And as always, old bits of bone, a shard of quartz, flower heads lopped off so I can check them against a field guide.

Thus supplied, I go out every afternoon now, like a miner starting for his shift. Only I am mining light, and my shovel and pick are my eyes. There is an urgency now about light. We have supper later in order to stay outdoors as long as possible, harvesting those last long beams that break across the cliffs to the west. I mark, every evening,

like a trapper learning a lucrative trail, the point on the top
of Little Whiskey where the sun sinks. It will move
backward every evening, away to the south, until it will be
no longer evening when the light disappears, but, in
December, the afternoon. We'll be herded indoors by the
darkness ever earlier. The night will be, finally, twice as
long as the day. Then we will have to live on our hoarded
stores of light. From the cellars where we have laid down a
reserve of bright light over water, we will have to drag up
the remains of afternoons and set a match to memory. The
light will have to come from inside our heads, like furnaces
stoked, if our eyes are to snap and sparkle then.

So we stay outdoors, finding excuses for lingering there
a little longer. Another length of log to split. Calculating the
weather for the next day. Watching the rabbits come out to
do their nervous nibbling. Bringing in the wash that's dried.

Hurry, hurry! This is the last. A close-out sale on the
sun. Gather ye sun-beams while ye may. Stock up now for
the winter. See! See! See! Stuff your eyes with light. Your
reflected light on the lake like a beaten metal bridge. Your
refracted light bending around rocks and tree boles, over the
cliff edge. Your diffused light filtering through leaves
growing more translucent every day as the opaque sap sinks
down into darkness. The light on the black cat's back,
soaked up like suet. The light on the underside of gulls,
gliding silvery in the upper air. The light on faces squinting
at the sun, in eyes whose irises bloom with blue as the
pupils contract to a central black period.

David has an iris cut away into a comma from a
childhood injury. Because of this, the pupil cannot contract
within the eye, thus causing him to squint, lopsided, at the
light. Otherwise the light would pour in through that ever
open chute, blinding the retina with too much of a good
thing.

He is, constitutionally, a world-devourer anyway. More
wood, he wants. Or more time. More music, more fire in the
stove. It's only fitting he should have more light too.

I have been watching for cocoons. The caterpillars
should be spinning them now. I understand that within the
walls of its long house, the caterpillar eventually turns to
mush, to a simple homogeneous goo, undifferentiated and

thickly liquid. Then, slowly, over the winter, it reconstitutes itself into what it will become. Butterflies and moths are not magic. Their mode of transformation is thorough and slow. Disintegration, dissolution, slop. And finally, delicate, unforeseen wings.

I lie in bed and look up at the receding convexities of logs that make up the walls of our cabin, and at the three long, bare tree boles that make the roof beams. It occurs to me that we live, literally, in a body of death. A shelter made of skinned, stacked-up tree bodies. As they have dried over the years, they have split inward. Inch-wide cracks spiral their length, letting me see inside their splintery corpses. Across the round roof beams lie rough-sawn planks that make the ceiling. The grain in the planks arches like the whorls of giant fingerprints.

How many Douglas fir, fifty feet high or better, fell for this edifice?

I live in a charnel house made of golden bones. Long, straight, lovely femurs. I like to run my hand along their slick round surfaces. I never tire of looking at the split sides hanging over my head, speckled with dark, concentric eyes where limbs were lopped off. It is a house made of beautiful bones.

An old colonial church I visited last year in central New Mexico is purported to have the bodies of over two hundred faithful members sealed up in its five-foot-thick adobe walls. My own cabin has that in common with the church. It is built of the bodies of firs at least as faithful as those Spanish and Indian souls. I take a certain comfort from the faithful corpses of firs, rising around me like ribs.

Yesterday was the first full day, officially, of autumn. We went to Riverton to buy tires for winter driving. The light was good, both going and coming back. Where farmers were cutting hay, the irrigated fields glowed green against the red clay or dun dirt. The irrigation ditches divide the fields in definite lines. One's eyes eat up green, literally. The human eye has more color receptors for green than any other color. And here on these arid plains and slopes where the sagebrush makes only the merest suggestion of a gray-green, the eyes get starved for their basic food.

But even the native grasses are greener now, after the melting snowfall, than they were when we first came three weeks ago. The alfalfa fields are a flagrant emerald. From the highway one sees the mowers moving across the fields steadily, leaving the fields stubbled where they have passed and where the cut hay is piled up in windrows like broad crayon marks. I think the mowers must like this job, it is so complete, so patterned. Later the hay will be boxed in neat bales; the grass will dry to the native colors of the region.

All this labor is enacted on the high, broad Wind River valley rimmed with blue mountains. Everything in this light that is perfectly balanced now between night and day appears lifted up, exalted. It is as though these laborers perform their work on a colossal stage, lit for a drama. Around and across the fields they go, laying down their lines precisely. It makes me want to applaud their show. Do they feel like performers out on this high floor, thrust up to the roots of heaven?

Why do these people stick with a life that appears to provide so few rewards for such demanding labor? Not many, in fact, do. The whole, vast rectangle of Wyoming contains less than half a million people. The land simply does not support many mouths. Those who live here in the mountains must contrive ways of making a living.

Every kind of work this country offers is only seasonal, from summer dude ranching to outfitting to trapping to logging. The iron mine in Atlantic City is open only sporadically. Even the Indians centuries ago never lived here year around.

So the present year-round residents must piece together a patchwork subsistence. I know a woman who combines surveying work for the highway department, cooking for a dude ranch, and gathering elk antlers from the mountain meadows for six cents a pound. The man who brought our firewood moved here from the east several years ago with his family when he discovered he had multiple sclerosis. He and his sons cut and haul wood for those others who winter over. His wife cuts hair. One way and another, those who want to stay badly enough find a way to finagle a living out of the land and one another. The aquatic biologist, who works for the Audubon camp during the summer, cooks for loggers until the weather shuts the camps down; then she

cleans houses during the winter. People who own land
board horses for the summer residents.

But anyone who winters over finds himself living off the
hunting economy. The farmers may raise a crop of hay, but
it's the elk, the deer, the antelope, the moose, and the
mountain sheep that make Wyoming thrive.

Yesterday we made an excursion into the Absoraka
range, up Horse Creek to Double Cabins on the
convergence of Frontier Creek and Wiggins Fork. We spent
the day hiking up and down the wide rocky riverbed in the
brilliant autumn weather.

Almost everyone up in that high glacial basin, except us,
is a hunter. The camps of outfitters with their four-horse
trailers clogged the camping areas.

We met two men in camouflage suits and backpacks who
had been bow-hunting for two weekends. They had rolled
out of their sleeping bags at four that morning to cross the
rough riverbed that spreads out half a mile wide at the fork.
They had scrambled up the scree on the far side of the
river and through the spruce cascading down the steep
slopes of Wiggins Peak. But the elk evaded them by
scrambling even higher, up above treeline to the rock
pinnacles eroded by wind and water into intricate vertical
organ pipes. The elk know all the crevices that make good
hiding places, places a man burdened with a thirty-pound
pack, a large bow, and a quiver full of arrows has trouble
maneuvering into.

The mountains are, among other things, a place where
people come to kill. For at least a couple of months out of
the year, the creeks and draws and ridges resound with the
loose metallic rattle of horse trailers and four-wheel-drive
pickups. The trails farther in are hammered with the hoof
marks of packhorses. Outfitters' rigs are parked in front of
gas stations and grocery stores down in town; sometimes
game carcasses are tied to them.

It was not always this way in the mountains. The plains
were the original haunt of both game and hunters. Many
species, grizzlies included, have taken refuge in the
mountains during the last 150 years as agriculture took their
habitat, but their original home was the broad expanse of
the high plains and river valleys.

Now the killing is done at higher altitudes. And for different reasons.

For most, the hunt's primary value lies in ritual. There are vestments. Down vests, billed caps. The liturgical colors of the season are either the army green of camouflage or day-glo orange of high visibility—sometimes a strange, contradictory combination of the two. The high priests of the hunt are the outfitters and they have the proper scorn of the clergy toward the laity they lead onto the unfamiliar ground. They are the servants and hirelings of the hunters, charged with cooking their meals and providing them with whatever comforts can be afforded in the unpredictable wilderness; but also they are the loremasters, the ones who know the trails, know the quarry, assess the portents. Like any priests, they have to put up with congregations of initiates, enthusiasts whose fervor only flares sporadically, who want the ritual but not the discipline.

As I watch them at the grocery store buying beer or packages of cookies, I wonder what the ritual means precisely, what it validates, what passageway into what world it provides. Is there some reality, some mystery that looms in the West that must be confronted? What is this ritual of killing that the mountains host every autumn?

I do not ask the question out of moralism. Here, where death is a big part of reality, one cannot object to seeing dead animals. Even Thoreau had sudden whims to eat hedgehogs raw.

But one does detect a certain patch of rot in the ritual from time to time. Those who make a quick foray into the mountains to kill a creature they see through a telescopic lens despise the reality that resides in these mountains. By subjugating the mountains to the artifacts of their own world, they hope to prove the potency of the life they have chosen, one of known quantities. They come to exact a tribute from the mountains like foreign potentates. They carry home the ram's horns or the moose antlers and call them trophies. The trophies prove that the skill of man—or at least the precision of his instruments—outdoes the skill of beasts. Death is therefore at man's disposal. There's nothing to be afraid of. No reality, no mystery greater than man himself.

Maybe. Although the weather, that as yet untamed foe, sometimes does a hunter in, coming upon him unexpectedly.

And sometimes they do themselves in. Hunters have been known to circle around a trail to outwit their quarry only to find they have come upon their base camp and shot their own horses. By the end of the season there is almost always some case in court over a camp murder.

Maybe also the desperation of the ritual shows it has not actually resolved the fears. For true ritual demands an exchange. One must bring an offering to the altar to receive a blessing. Perhaps man the hunter can compensate for his constitutional slow-footedness by the speed of his weapons without losing the value of the ritual. But some energy has to be exchanged for the reciprocity of the ritual to work. The hunter must survive on the same terms as his quarry. He must accept its world as substantial reality, must meet the demands of the mountain in the same way the beast does, if his killing is to mean anything at all.

The bow-hunter yesterday had made a considerable expenditure of energy for no more than a far-off glimpse of his prey. But his own mortality was clear to him as he sat sweating and exhausted on the river-scoured stump. The limitations of his body were plain. If he had in fact shot an elk, the game rules made up by the Forest Service would have required him to dress and quarter it on the site and then to pack it out on his back. The effort required to pack several hundred pounds of fresh meat down a mountain trail is considerable. But he would perhaps have been carrying away also the blessing that particular altar has to offer. Even in his failure, in his aching bones and weary blood, he carried away more than he knew. A certain knowledge of the death he had come there for.

October

I said earlier that the hunters don't bring anything to the
altar, but they do: money. Lots of it. Enough to supply a
good part of Wyoming's economy. A ten-day pack trip starts
at $1800 and can go up to $3500 per person. This entitles
the purchaser to pick-up service from the airport in Riverton
or Jackson, a horse to ride up through the mountain passes,
a tent, probably a rain poncho, meals cooked in the open, a
hunting guide to point him in the right direction, someone
to dress the kill and transport the meat to a processing
plant. The outfitting crew takes care of the horses, cooks the
meals, cleans up the camp, finds the game, nursemaids the
dudes. On public lands a guide is limited to only two
hunters. At the end of the ten days, I imagine the $1800
looks like little enough for the trouble.

There are more antelope than people in Wyoming. Last
year almost 68,000 were killed during the hunting season, a
third of those by out-of-state hunters who drive for two days
across the mid-plains to reach the mountains. People who
live in Wyoming are not so eager to hunt pronghorn
antelope. Great herds of these gazelle-like prairie goats,

often a hundred or more, graze all year in the pastures and on hillsides like cows. There seems little sport in hunting such a familiar, almost domestic animal. Mule deer are more popular with resident hunters, especially in the eastern part of the state. They are more elusive and don't travel in large herds like antelope.

It is elk that Wyoming hunters prize most, though, both for their meat and for their impressive antlers. Elk stay up in the high country until the snow finally forces them down to the clear feeding grounds in late fall. For such large animals, however—an adult elk can be six feet at the shoulder—they are surprisingly slippery. Less than a third of the hunters with elk permits ever get one, even though the state has the largest elk refuge in the world. Hunters are more successful killing the shaggy, bovine moose than the elegant elk. Even though moose with their palmate antlers are much rarer animals, ninety percent of the moose permits are filled every year. Still, even with their knack for outsmarting their predators, over 18,000 elk were killed by hunters in Wyoming last year—or "harvested" as the Game and Fish Department report describes it.

Yesterday we went hiking up on Little Whiskey. When
we climbed out onto the first high open meadow, the only
other creature moving across the elevated stage was a coyote
right on the rim of the exposed slope above us. We could
hear the barking calls from his den down among the rocks.
He ranged back and forth across the slope, sniffing the
ground, with no apparent concern for our presence, although
he kept his distance as we moved on up higher. Finally, he
disappeared on the far side of the hill.

We were searching the ground for the rare blue rocks,
shaped like brains or cauliflower heads, that Little Whiskey
is known for. We picked up and discarded a dozen rocks,
trying to find the perfect specimen. Only a crow, raucous
and common, gave us any company.

We climbed, our eyes still on the ground, until we came
to the place where the coyote had stood watching us. Then
we turned, angling off the blank slope into the stand of
large, stumpy short-needled pines. September's snows still
lay in among the trees, sifted over with brown needles. We
picked our way over the deadfall and through the trees till
we came out again on the highest clearing we were likely to
reach that day.

Over the Absorakas to the northeast a storm was
brewing. And to the west, back up our own canyon, as
though in echo, another had begun. This was no mountain
scene ever put on a postcard. This was the mountains when
they are serious, with the solemn spectacle of a storm
moving across huge expanses of void. Austere as space,
fierce with wind and cold.

We started down. You can carry away a glimpse of these
titanic powers to the cabin below and wonder at them there,
but you don't want to get caught in a storm on an exposed
mountain slope. You feel misery, not grandeur, when the
weather closes in. The vertiginous expanses disappear, and
there is only the blur of snow whipping in front of your
face and the wind cutting you close.

We slid through the down side of the snowfields,
turning back a moment, when we came to a level place, to
watch the huge approach of the waters over the earth. Then,
over the next rise, we suddenly saw what we should have
expected, a large herd of Rocky Mountain bighorn sheep.
They are skittish animals, but they seemed as unconcerned

with us as the coyote had been. Although their sentinels kept an eye on us, they moved no farther off. They stood their ground. The Game and Fish Department has the area posted as their winter range, and they seem to know they are safe there.

There were, however, no rams with full-curled horns among this herd. They are the ones designated as legal targets for hunters and have left the herd for higher territory until hunting season is over. The lambs, now in midsized adolescence, darted across the patches of snow from one feeding group to another. Without their movement the unaided and unexpecting eye might not have noticed the herd at all, even though only a half mile of clear, empty air separated us. They were precisely the color of the bare patches of ground. Less than two hundred of this species were taken as trophies last year.

I wonder about the so-called harvesting of these animals, the wording used in Game and Fish Department reports. It reminds me of war vocabulary with its official talk of "friendly fire," terminology that refuses to name the reality. Why do we find it so hard to say *kill*, whether the object of that verb is human or elk? One can harvest grain, harvest fruit, harvest hay. But to speak of harvesting moose is a travesty; it diminishes both the hunted and the hunter.

The game population in Wyoming is carefully controlled. Only so many permits per species are issued each year, proportionate to the estimated numbers in the herds. This is so that Wyoming will not run out of the natural resource that attracts so many out-of-state spenders, but also because the animals need to be culled for the health of the herd. Bighorn sheep would mire in a biological sink if their numbers went unchecked. Of course, they have their natural predators that cull the old and sick animals, but why should coyotes have all the fun?

David and I wonder a lot about hunters and hunting. Is it any harder to kill an antelope than a cow? Are their large swimming brown eyes any less reproachful? We haven't had a lot of experience with conscious killing. A few domestic rabbits and chickens, round-eyed fish, a snake, flies and mosquitoes. Does killing count more if the animals are bigger? Or if you are willing to pay $200 a day for the opportunity to kill them? Does it count less if you eat the meat than if you merely cut the head off to hang on the wall? And what about the instinctual necessity to hunt? Are those without that drive lacking something essentially human?

On September 29 we had our second big snowstorm. Since then we have had snow about every three days. It begins to look as though there will be no Indian summer, no long winey days filled with that late peculiar amber light. There may be instead only a steady increase of cold and wind that strips the dead leaves from the alders along the river bank. Already the birds are vacating the landscape. We only see an occasional merganser or a gull or Clark's nutcracker now.

We have about three cords of wood already stacked along the wall of the cabin. But with the omens of an early winter rushing upon us, David has gotten anxious. We can't drive across the meadow to retrieve the dead trees he's cut down on the far side of the lake until the ground freezes. This frets him. What if unusual early deep snows should come, burying the logs, making them inaccessible? "Now is the time for gathering wood." He says it like "Today is the day of salvation."

So, after lunch we go out to the battlefield where the trees have been felled, carrying our weapons: the chainsaw, the bucksaw, the axe and wedges. The chainsaw fills the nuclear weapons category in this arsenal. Neither of us like it. It is alien to us, as much a weapon against ourselves as against the wood or the cold. A slip, a stumble, and there could be not just a wound in the foot or the hand, but a severed artery, a lost limb. Also, for all its supposed energy-saving, it demands a great deal of care and attention. One pours oil into its bowels constantly to assuage its foul temper. The chain gets caught in a knot and flies off. It has to be taken into town to be sharpened. The starting mechanism has to be replaced at a price that would almost have bought another cord of wood.

Knowing this, we have resolved to use it sparingly. In fact, this is our last day of working with it. Two stumps remain to be cut to a lower, more decent level. They are both gnarled and knotted and too big for the bucksaw to handle. To satisfy a sense of order, they must be sheared off, cannot be left looking so brutalized above the ground. With the power of omens hanging over us we begin. The chainsaw screams and moans like the soul of all machinery tortured past its capacity. Metal fatigue takes on an audible voice.

And for its part, the tree gives up grudgingly, taking as much as possible of an alien, mechanical world's resources down with it. The chainsaw wails. The tree silently spits out its innards in damp sawdust. It has been dead for some years. One of its three boles corded together here at the base is rotten and punky at the core. Still it puts up a fight. It answers the fury of the chainsaw with the steady resistance of its weight. Even after it is cut clear through, it sits there, refusing to fall. We have to heave it off its foundation.

Then we stand and look at one another in the sudden silence. Once more the lake water laps against the shore a few feet away. The wind soughs through the trees. A gull calls like a cat. These sounds seem more distinct, stand out, quite literally, in relief against the blessed air the chainsaw had filled with agony. It's over. We screw the safety tip back on the blade and cover it with the plastic sock.

We have been, once again, caught in the middle between our inexcusable human necessities and our superfluity in creation. Between the dominion we once had over the earth and the shabby devices we now try to maintain that position with. If we are indeed the lords of creation, we have a strange way of showing it. Inelegant, vulgar, obtrusive, boorish. The more sophisticated we become, the more crass our tools. We cannot create an implement with the simplicity and fittingness of a nuthatch's beak. And our tools offend us, harm us, as much as they do the silence.

So what are we to do, short of obliterating our offensive selves? We cannot deny our need for heat during the winter. If it weren't the wood, it would be coal, power plants, strip mines. It is always something. Something coming between us and the world.

The best we can do, David says, and I believe him, is to accept our necessities with humility.

The most wholesome food is not caught with net or
snare, said William Blake.

That may be, although I think a net or snare would be
preferable to some other ways. Yesterday a friend and I
went into town to the post office. The curbs were lined with
pickups and hunting rigs. Several of them had carcasses, stiff
as logs, in back. I counted two moose and a good many elk.
They were already gutted, of course, their bellies split and
the ribs curling around a dark cavern like a rotted-out tree
trunk. The feet were cut off halfway up the lower bones,
leaving the legs stiff, mutilated stumps in the air. The
heads, as always, were thrown back. Often the antlers were
already sawn off too.

On the way home we saw a truck with a moose in back,
already skinned but with the antlers still on. The muscles,
covered with their slick integument, gleam silvery and pale
pink in the pickup bed. A denuded moose ghost.

At church this morning there was a woman who runs a
hunting camp up in the mountains every fall. She's thin and
wiry and lives the rest of the year in Illinois. She complains
about the weather; there's been two feet of snow at her
camp. She's been glad to get "her hunters" out alive, she
says.

I feel my stomach begin to knot, the back of my tongue
to buckle under the weight of unspoken words and unasked
questions. To question hunting here is like not voting
Republican. It's taken for granted that you do—unless you
absolutely can't afford it.

There is no humility in her western hat with its feather
fringe. No necessity in her supple leather vest with the
coyote fur collar. There is no need, no need. Not even
ferocity. Only play-acting.

I thought last night about particular animals I have seen
killed near me and on my behalf. The hens in the high-
fenced chicken yard I remember from childhood. Mother
used to wring their necks grimly, her teeth clenched and
her nostrils flaring until—after an agonizing flurrying of
feathers—the vertebrae snapped and the hen flopped
headlessly about the yard for several seconds. After it was
scalded and plucked and the pinfeathers singed off, she fried
it crisp. The meat was pure delight. Nothing processed
through the supermarket compares with it today. But she

would not have flaunted the hen's feathers in her hat or dangled its feet around her neck.

I also remember the hogs my grandfather killed on frosty fall mornings and hung up on a singletree from an oak branch. The carcass spread pink and white, still steaming in the chill November morning air from its stored body heat. The chunks of fat crackled and spat in a black iron pot on an open fire as they melted into lard. That night we feasted on chitlings roasted on coals in the fireplace. It was a special treat.

These kitchen-killings fascinated me as a child. Not that I could have taken the hen's small head in my own hand with enough confidence to grasp it for wringing. But I always stood to the side and watched, blinking, as the body spun through the air in a slow arc. The futile burlesque of the headless corpse flopping in the dust and leaves I found both funny and sad. Perhaps I watched simply to savor this strange new combination of feelings.

The hogs I never actually watched die, although I heard them squeal. I think my grandfather must have shot them with his .22. But I watched, again fascinated, as the carcass was peeled, deftly, expertly, of its thick hide; was hoisted; and as the guts, the lobed liver, and all the shining, mighty, variegated entrails came spilling into the washtub. There is nothing quite like fresh-killed meat.

For children, death is not a matter of morality; it is a mystery, like sex. This is why the pity they may feel for a struggling slaughtered animal does not deter them from eating its meat. On the farm no one ever tried to shield me from the sight of slaughter.

The painter, Marc Chagall, had a grandfather in Russia who was the butcher for the Jewish settlement in the little town of Vitebsk before the Revolution. As a child, he too watched as his grandfather first said the required prayer and then slaughtered the cow.

> The prayer is hardly over before he holds her neck back and runs the steel into her throat.
> Torrents of blood.
> Impassively, the dogs and hens wait around for a drop of blood, a morsel that might accidentally fall to the ground.
> Nothing can be heard but their clucking, their

rustling, and grandfather's sighs amid the torrents
of fat and blood.

And you, little cow, naked and crucified, you
are dreaming in heaven. The glittering knife has
raised you to the skies.

Silence.

The intestines uncoil and the pieces fall apart.
The skin drops off.

Pink, blood-red pieces pour out. Steam rises.

What a job to have on one's hands.

I feel like eating meat.

Some time ago, David and I, much against his
inclinations, kept chickens. Originally they were for eggs,
but when the dogs got at them, killing some and tearing up
the others, we ended up having to finish them all off. Or
rather, he had to. I did the plucking and cooking and
storing. This time I was not fascinated.

Nor did I watch more than once when he took an iron
bar and, holding a rabbit by its hind legs, struck it behind
the neck. He did the skinning and cleaning too. Then I took
the long-muscled bodies and dismembered them for the
frying pan. Adults, with all too much knowledge of good and
evil, are no longer fascinated with this kind of death.

On the farm a certain grimness pervaded the grownups
until the killing was over. There was not any particular
pride in the killing. No one took pleasure in this grim
necessity. "What a job to have on one's hands." There were
no extravagant tales, no swaggering, no special fashions to
wear. Only a certain tension until the job was done. Then
relief spread through them. There was work to do, and meat.

I don't understand why God accepted Abel's slaughtered
animals and not Cain's tidy bundles of toasted grain. Is he a
god of gore, a cosmic carnivore, antivegetarian? Or was it
his way of rubbing our noses in our own necessity?

The alders are growing rusty around the edges of the
lake. No wind yesterday or today, but sunshine, so that the
lakes themselves are like mirrors of blued stove metal.

While the laundry was drying on the line I went down
to the little beach where the boats are dragged up onto the
shingle. I walked up the beach a ways, idly watching for
tracks in the wet sand. The sun laid out a bridge across the
water. It hasn't been this hospitable—warm and windless—
in days.

I caught a strange noise out in the water and turned suddenly to see four sleek heads staring at me from the lake. Otters. They disappeared in four dark parabolas as soon as I noticed them, but surfaced again a few feet further on, chuffing and snorting. By some means they manage to get their heads remarkably high out of the water, peer about, and then swim on, nose first, until the notion takes them to dive again, long pointed tail last.

A friend of ours has also seen the otters on the large flat rocks that lie across the outlet from Trail Lake. One otter was larger than the rest, the mother possibly. They watched my friend curiously, but when she came closer to fish in her usual spot, they scrammed. On the rocks she noticed their droppings and the dark blood and scales from the whitefish and suckers they feed on there. David saw one yesterday too, on the far bank. They have burrows in the banks, but with underwater approaches like beaver dams. Also, they have a range of up to fifteen miles. They may go farther downstream this winter when the creek freezes.

This morning when I came into the cabin I use for writing, the floor was littered with dead flies. Every night for over a week now the temperature has dropped into the twenties, but still the flies hang on, skirring over the windowpanes, clumping together wherever the sun warms the sill. Like any other creature, they cling to life. But I don't see them as pathetic figures, the way Virginia Woolf described the moth dying on her windowsill: "a tiny bead of pure life" struggling valiantly against the "indifferent, impersonal" power of death. She chose a moth, a fluttery, sympathetic sort of creature to eulogize, not a big, buzzing, irritating housefly. Why does it suit the romantic temperament to make us all out to be innocent victims of implacable doom?

The creek has sunk about two inches in one day. One of the boulders at the bridge on which a bright chartreuse moss grows has that much of its side exposed by afternoon, the moss still damp above the water line. The heavy snows we had earlier have melted quickly higher up in the mountains and have kept the stream well filled till now. But we have had about five straight days of dry and warming weather so that these veins in the mountains are dwindling. The snowmelt seems to have run out at last. Our friend, the one who saw the otters, predicts that we'll be able to walk across the creek from rock to dry rock before it freezes over.

I work sometimes in the study cabin in the afternoons now when the sun comes full in the west window. But the tail end of my working day gets chopped off shorter and shorter. The cliff face of Little Whiskey, on the other side of the creek and the road, blocks the sun earliest here. A shadow starts from the base of the gold and buff sandstone. Its first bite is the road. The next is the stream. It creeps up the near bank, across the twenty feet between the stream and the cabin, and then swallows the cabin itself. However warm the sun has been, the chill that falls when it goes is immediate and noticeable. That shadow is The End of each day. Its gray body moves, visibly and steadily, across the sagebrush, the moraines, the other cabin, the east-turning bend of the creek, the meadow beyond that, out onto Ring Lake, and having swallowed all that, climbs the eastern ridge, the whole bowl of the valley filling up with shadow, until, spilling over the top of the ridge, it is night.

Northwestward, up the crack the canyon makes in our horizon, we can still see the sun on the Absorakas, the snow on the Ramshorn turning pink. That peak also gets the sun first every morning, a full hour before any light reaches down to us in our gray declivity.

As the year runs out and dries up, the shadow will come sooner, slinking up a half a minute, a minute, two minutes earlier every afternoon. Less light. Like the creek with less water. Less, less, less. We'll huddle in what patches and pools of light we can find as it moves across the cabin floor, like fish hunting water while the river sinks.

In the late afternoon a whole convoy of hunting rigs goes up the road to the trailhead into the Fitzpatrick Wilderness. Three pickups, one with a small travel trailer, one with a six-horse trailer, one with a camper shell, and a four-wheel-drive van. The hunting season, both for elk and moose, runs on till the end of November. It started about the first of October here, earlier farther north. Sixty days each for moose and elk. Antelope season is only ten days at a time and moves from place to place, patchwork, across the state during the fall. The failing rivers and streams, the growing hours of darkness, the cold, the hunters—they all come together. Harvest time.

We go up the Bomber Trail this morning, a trail named for a World War II plane that crashed here in the mountains in the forties. The story is that a crew was returning from a training mission back to a station farther west across the mountains when they decided to take a side trip up that particular canyon to scare up some elk. People still make the five-mile ascent to carry away bits of broken metal as souvenirs from the crash site beside a waterfall.

At the base of the trail we find four separate hunting camps set up. You would think you had run into a bunch of Buddhist monks, there's so much saffron orange around. Several children with rifles slung over their shoulders are being settled on ponies by the outfitters. Older men sit in lawn chairs around the campfires, coffee mugs in their hands. The wranglers are working hard.

The trailhead is so crowded we decide to take an alternate route that follows Torrey Creek. At the horse ford farther up the creek we come upon a lone outfitter clearing the crossing of windfall brush for his group. Our path will not cross those of the hunting parties again today though. They take Glacier Trail, which ascends steeply across the face of an avalanche to get to the high hunting grounds faster. We will only be rising with the east fork of Torrey Creek about 1500 feet till we get to Bomber Falls.

The sun is at full strength, but where it has not yet reached, the ground is filigreed with frost. The fallen leaves and tiny alpine plants are rimed around the edges with white lace. The light, to our left across the creek, catches on the spider webs stretched from limb to rock to twig like so many high-lines gleaming and sure. Insects are surprisingly hardy. How can they survive so many nights of hard frost? They are few—spiders, a bee, cassis flies hovering over the water—but all the more noticeable for having survived this long. All of us are sucking the marrow out of the splintered ends of the year's bones.

Farther up the trail, where it climbs through dense Douglas fir trees, we run into an officious squirrel. He is burying cones in the soft black loam under the trees. He

gives us one warning glance and turns back to his job till
he has all his treasure buried. Then he runs up another
tree, clear to the top, and begins harvesting the cones there.
And harvesting is quite literally what he is doing. He checks
the end of each branch for the quality cones, this year's
crop, nips them neatly loose, and then pitches them out and
down with his front paws. Now he is chirking in a
continuous stream of irascibility. Every explosion of sound
propels his arced body forward several inches. After he has
gleaned three treetops, we move on. You can only watch
someone work for so long.

But we have to stop frequently. David's asthma makes
breathing harder in the thin air. We lean on boulders and
look through binoculars at mountain sheep across the valley
and higher up on the snowfields, the sky bright behind
them.

Farther along the trail we meet, unexpectedly, a hunter
on foot. He has his grandson with him. He is a short man, a
local worker, and in the brief exchange we make as we pass
on the trail, I see his face is soft and kind. A man who
gathers his family about him.

He reminds me of the man who runs the meat lockers
in town where the skinned game are cut up to specification.
He was about this height. His face was eager and gentle.
And his eyes swam palely in weariness from the harvest.

Our summer friend has gone for the winter. No near
neighbor now, not at least for a mile and a half. No need to
watch for car lights coming along the road when she's been
out after dark. More warmth withdrawn, body warmth, face
gleams, eye lights.

Up above us the empty cabins sit on the hillsides,
facing out, like so many staring graves. The power has been
turned off, the water lines drained. The beds are waiting,
the chairs pulled back. In summer the cabins are full of
visitors from several states. Figures move among the rocks
and along the lakes then, various and clamorous. Now
there's only the place itself and memory: last summer, three
summers ago, the nun from St. Louis, the Canadian civil
servant, the teacher from the east. Walking among the cabins
is like wandering through a cemetery. They are memorials
now, not habitations.

A half mile away in our cabin at night I listen to the wind and think about the empty cabins brooding above us.

On the road going into church this Sunday morning we see a minor flock of magpies clustered around a rock. They must have found some carrion to have gathered in such a congregation. When we draw up even with them we see what it is—the hacked off ribs of an elk, white curves intersticed with pink and red. The magpies have profited from the hunters. They don't complain.

At church the vicar speaks of peace and bombs. Since he is a short man, he has been requested by the bishop's committee to stand on a box behind the pulpit. He looks down at us and then up, diagonally, into the back corner of the church. His face is pained. He is coming close to middle age. The world hurts him. He wears it like a hair shirt.

I listen to him talk about peace and think about the magpies and the elk ribs. I don't want to end like the elk, one last startled goggle of terror, the last bit of information imprinting the brain about betrayal. I only wish we could end the war on the elk too, make a treaty, come to terms. Maybe these could be the terms: Carnivores can kill only other carnivores. Tit for tat. Sweets to the sweet. How would magpie taste? Leave the elk to their browse and berries. Let's go after the grizzly. Try domesticating him like chickens and cows.

I see the otters late in the afternoon. One has a fish in its mouth. Two aquatic carnivores linked in the food chain.

When we came to the mountains to spend the winter we brought our cat with us. She is a rather small animal with long black hair that looks rusty in direct sunlight. She's finicky about the weather and doesn't like to go outdoors if it's cold or the wind is blowing. We brought her along with the idea that she'd be good for catching mice. Even in summer when people are here, the small deer mice invade the cabins and make themselves at home among the store-bought provisions in the kitchen cabinets. In winter, of course, the incentive to find cozy accommodations is even greater. So we brought along kitty for the express purpose of doing our dirty work for us. For hunting.

And she has not disappointed us. She likes to patrol the closed-in porch after dark and will sit by the front door until someone opens it and lets her out. She had been out for an hour or more on the porch, poking among the fishing tackle, saw, and snowshoes the first night here, when I remembered to let her in. I opened the door and in she trotted, mouse whiskers dangling from one side of her mouth and a long, thin, gray tail from the other, as obviously pleased with herself as any successful outfitter.

By now, however, the new has worn off the basic mouse hunt. She has learned that the fun can be made to last longer by not killing her quarry immediately. Instead, she likes to play a kind of hockey, using the mouse as the puck.

Last night we had already gone to bed and turned off the light when we remembered kitty was still out on the porch. David got up and opened the door in the dark to let her in. He was just crawling back into bed when there was a skittering, a dash, a muffled struggle. We both knew at once what had happened. Kitty had brought in a mouse, a still very live mouse, to amuse herself with for the evening.

David climbs out of bed again. Turns on the light. Grabs up the broom. Obviously the cat and the mouse must be separated or there will be no sleeping. He makes a lunge, swats at kitty and her mouse. She retreats beneath the table. He sweeps her out with the broad side of the broom. She leaps onto a chair. He runs into the stove. I laugh. He shouts. Kitty leaps down again, dropping the mouse as she lands. The mouse runs—where? Quite clearly behind a sofa, for the huntress is now hunched at one corner there, motionless. David considers moving the sofa and then decides against it. Perhaps the mouse can take care of itself till morning. He turns off the light and comes back to bed muttering.

This morning, kitty is still hunkered immobile at her post. More confident in the morning light, David moves one end of the sofa. Out dashes the mouse. The cat pounces. David hesitates. Moral ambiguity washes over his face. Then he grabs the broom again and beats off the cat. He scoops the battered mouse onto the dustpan and takes it outside. There he sets it carefully on the ground and watches as it dashes off into the sagebrush.

Luckily, kitty's level of conscious understanding is not

very high or she would be asking us all sorts of
embarrassing questions.

This afternoon I have a bone to pick. A lamb bone. I sit
at the kitchen table slicing away the meat from a joint our
decamped neighbor roasted last week and bequeathed to us
when she was cleaning out her refrigerator. The color of the
meat on the surface is taupe, a kind of brownish gray.
Nearer the center it is pink. The fat is the color of eggshell,
though the integument that encases the muscles is grayer.
Here and there are tendons that have turned a translucent
amber from the heat of cooking. And last of all the bone. A
thin, graceful clavicle, lovely as a sail on a boat. At the ends
it thickens with marrow, but in the center it is pared to
only a shell's thinness so that the light comes through it. At
one end it has been sawn off straight. At the other end is a
socket that articulates with the next bone, a rounded ball
that fits perfectly into its receptacle. I twist the two bones
apart, the ligaments that hold them in place splitting loose.
The white ball joint looks like a suddenly sprung-up
mushroom, still damp. I lick my fingers, dump the hunks of
meat into a stewpot. The bones go in the garbage. *Agnus
dei.* Behold the lamb of God.
The world is at a stand off between Francis of Assisi
and Ernest Hemingway.

During the night the wind blew fierce. I woke up and
listened in the moonless dark, wondering about the creatures
that must be huddled in their holes against it. The Wyoming
wind is like the feudal wars of the Middle Ages, always
there, ready to break out and ride roughshod over your
carefully built up fence rows and furrows, ravaging your
thatch, its terrible, far-ranging powers trampling and
uprooting your small plans for survival. All unawares and
uncaring. We creatures can only bend our backs to it and
hope to ride it out. How do the birds manage to cling to
the branches?
This morning the leaves are noticeably fewer on the
river alders and water birch. We begin to be able to see
through their branches clear to the lake. It looks like mid-
November already, and we're only two-thirds into October.
In the afternoon I walk along the lake and see where

the north wind has splashed the water on the south shore, up onto the rocky shelf. There is a thick coating of ice on tree limbs, twigs, driftwood, and stones, which has not melted by sundown. Tomorrow it will be thicker.

On the east shore there is no ice. The otters have obviously been here today. They have sunned themselves on the big rocks out in the water. Their scats—wads of splintered fish bones and scales held together with green ooze—are still fresh.

The lichen on a granite rock, a brilliant orange copper, echoes exactly the turning wild rose leaves that lie against it. I startle a phalarope who runs waterward on long legs and then takes to the air, heading south.

Amplified across the lake, the rumble of the four-wheel-drive battle wagons keeps on. Our road, rocky and arduous, is seldom used after summer, but the traffic of the hunting outfitters makes it a noisy campaign highway. This must be the way noncombatants live in wartime. Going about their business as best they can, their heads down, yet unable to shut out the constant rumor of war.

I bring home a ghost bouquet clutched in my hand. Dried stalks of columbine, pentstemon, and gentian. They are the color of the dead flakes of flesh sloughed off from the skin in winter. I put them in a green bottle on the south windowsill where the light will shine through them as it shone through the thin part of the lamb bone.

The lake is fiercely, piercingly blue as I wander home. The sky trembles with light. In this blue domed bowl are stewed these mingled tokens of life and death.

Yesterday I wandered down by Trail Lake, looking in the shingle by the shore for arrow chips. I was standing still, contemplating the subtle, cupreous green of the water a few feet from shore, when a chipmunk came from behind a log and looked at me. The longitudinal black lines on his face and his backward pointing ears made him look finely foxlike.

"Hello," I said in a neighborly way. "Getting ready for winter?"

As though to answer my question he scurried down to the pebbly beach where several fir cones lay and began rolling them over like logs and searching their spikes for

kernels. He pulled the spikes out with his delicate front
paws and pared away the extra cellulose with his teeth.
Then he packed the kernels in his cheek.

Soon another of his clan appeared and descended onto
the beach, coming nose-to-nose with the first one. They
were, I thought at first, nuzzling one another. But no.
Suddenly the second chipmunk nipped the first, whereupon
the first ran off and up onto a rock, where he watched the
invader carry on with harvesting his cones.

The bully was so sure of himself that he came within
inches of my boot, totally unconcerned with a creature large
enough to do him a good deal of harm. There were, of
course, enough cones on the beach for two chipmunks. But
the pushing around seemed to be the point as much as the
provisioning.

This evening the vicar from the local church comes to
visit. He looks, if not yet a corpse, at least a soul suffering
acerbitas mortis, the bitterness of death. I've seen his face
already today in a picture I have of a burial scene from the
Grimani Breviary.

He's always wanted to be a race-car driver, he tells us.
On Sunday afternoons he drives to Crowheart, where he
provides the Eucharist for maybe two or three people. He
feels as though he buries the church every Sunday, over and
over again, like a bad dream that won't end.

The big Douglas fir that marked the beginning of the
trail up Little Whiskey is gone. We only noticed it yesterday
morning as we went along the road in the dawn light. It
had been a tall and spreading tree, easily distinguished from
its stunted or spindly neighbors on the dry exposed slope. It
had thrust itself—how many ages ago?—up through a crack
in a boulder. Now there is only a jagged stump about ten
feet high. At its feet lie its own green arms and head.

It is obvious now what must have brought the tree
down. Its exposed core is dark with rot. The outer rind of
healthy flesh is only six inches thick at the widest point.
Clear resin oozes like blood drops from this torn tissue. The
rest of its insides are either covered with white chalky mold
or, nearer the center, simply rotted dry, snuff-colored, and
crumbly. It fell toward the side where it had the thinnest

support. The crashed corpse stretches out for at least fifty
feet. Almost all its branches have splintered off, some driven
by the crash into the rocky soil. Its arms are still green, this
year's cones still on them.

This is one of the great mysteries about death. That in
the midst of life we are dying. That we start to die long
before we come crashing down. We live in bodies of death.
Death is not some future state. Right now, this moment, I
am dying. There is some spot in me, large like the core of
the fir tree or small like a few alveoli in the lungs, that has
lost the power to restore itself. The single event we call
death is only the last step in the process. One night a big
wind comes up and the rotted structures within are no
longer sufficient to withstand the stress, to tie body and soul
together.

David has come here to die, just as I have. The death
he desires is the refining of his vocation, a certain
purification of purpose. He needs pruning, he feels, of the
irrelevant undergrowth that is leaching away the fruits of his
life.

He remembers with longing his liturgical chores: being
a spearhead for the ascending songs and prayers of a
congregation, aimed toward God with the people like the
shaft of a spear at his back. But turning to face them—their
expectations, questions, assessments—he becomes distracted,
embroiled, forgets what he was about.

He feels like Moses, fled to the wilderness of Midian.
He has killed a man back in Egypt, a man he found
scathing God's people. A man who was himself. He has
buried that self in the sand, the self that strikes out of grief
and rage. Now he lives here in the Wyoming wilderness,
keeping a wary eye on every bush that might suddenly burst
into flames of speech. As they were for Moses, God's people
are both his bane and blessing.

And like Moses he stumbles, forgets words, is overwhelmed with a sense of stupidity and shame. Dyslocution
sweeps over him at odd moments like waves of nausea. In
midsentence his voice will suddenly falter and fail, like a
candle guttering out.

He is all too familiar with the story of Moses. He knows
he is not really safe here in Midian. Sooner or later, you
have to go back to Egypt. It is only a matter of time until

some bush speaks. And when it does, it will be to give him impossible instructions such as Moses received.

Can you really imagine going to strangers and, with a straight face, telling them I AM sent you? If they have any sense at all, they'll laugh you out of town.

Arnold Schoenberg, the twentieth-century Jewish composer, wrote an opera, *Moses und Aron*, which he was never able to complete to his satisfaction. It is about Moses, who is entrusted with the impossible task of verbalizing in human language to the people of Israel the name of God, the Word, the I AM. Being true to the content of that message necessarily ties up his tongue and tears apart any form that tries to contain it. Therefore, Moses must rely on Aaron, the silver-tongued accommodator willing to build a golden calf to relieve the people's intolerable anguish over an invisible God, a people who wanted to "see" what that Word meant.

"O my Lord, I am not an eloquent man, neither heretofore, nor since thou hast spoken unto thy servant: but I am slow of speech, and of a slow tongue." Is there any tongue fleet enough to say what God is? I don't blame Moses for balking. Only a fool would willingly take up the task of speaking God's unspeakable name. Unless, like Aaron, he hasn't really understood the impossibility of the task. God and his people are always at odds. The one in the middle, like Moses, gets caught in the squeeze.

If you say yes, however reluctantly, to I AM, the effort will kill you, and more than once. To get from Midian back to Egypt was in fact another death for Moses. "At an inn on the way I AM met him and sought to kill him." And it will be no different, I'm afraid, for us. Here we are at our wayside inn in the wilderness. I feel like Zipporah now, Moses' Midianite wife. "Surely," she told him, "you are a bridegroom of blood to me."

It's easy enough to talk about death in these immense terms. But we are not huge archetypal characters moving across some epic stage. We live the common life of creatures, a life full of good things to cling to. How is someone who still loves to laugh, read, think, whistle, pray, eat, travel, kiss, play Scrabble—how is he to die, even though he also carries around the atrophied tissue of a vocation in need of severe pruning?

So he goes on living, like the tree, a mixture of life and death. Alive, yet desiring death, surcease from his angry wounds. Wincing from pain in his outer extremities and nerve-endings, yet alive enough to desire the goodness of God. Light and shadow alternating like night and day.

Will it ever be any different? That is my question, one I keep to myself. Is sharing the death of Christ a matter of overcoming the shadow of death within us? Or is it a matter of finding a way to die? Or again, is it a matter of sustaining the insupportable burden of this body of death, of living with the death embedded in our living flesh?

The skies have been leaden for several days now. We have been unable to clock the sun's rising and setting. On sunny days I perform this task like a nurse charting an expiring patient's respiration and pulse rate. The hemisphere's plunge into darkness has slowed though. Whereas the sun used to rise about two minutes later each day, it is now down to less than a minute.

In the afternoon we make our trek over to the woodpile on the east side of the lake. The trunks of the dead trees we have sawed up lie in lengths. We are waiting for the ground to freeze so that we can drive a pickup across the meadow to bring them back to the cabin. But the smaller limbs, only as thick as an arm, still need chopping to stove length.

David lays about him with the axe. I pitch the hacked pieces into a pile. We pause from time to time to rest and wonder at the preternatural stillness of the lake. Once we look up onto the high meadow on top of Little Whiskey and count fifty-four bighorn sheep grazing. Fish are feeding too, making round dimples in the silvered surface of the water. The hatch of flies they're snapping up, however, are so small that nothing in the tackle box can match them.

At dusk it begins to rain. One always expects a storm around Halloween. Will this be it? It is still perfectly calm outside. Nothing moves except the placid rain falling.

At midnight the wind started to stir. Here comes Wyoming again, I thought. The gusts grow fierce against the windows. All through the night we hear the air suck through the stovepipe. But in the morning, no snow. North, through the V of the canyon, we see the whitened Absorakas. The snow stopped there.

We woke this morning to knifelike wind, cobalt skies, sunlight, and—trumpeter swans on the lake! Nine great snowy birds formed a white flotilla on the blue waters, their smudge-colored cygnets threading through them. We plunged out into the wind with our binoculars at once, but they moved off farther toward the center of the lake, keeping a cautious distance. The DuNoir valley north of here is a known nesting ground for trumpeter swans, but rarely do any appear in this canyon.

We had thought this a rare enough sight, but later, on his way to town, David saw sixty of the swans down on Torrey Lake, a fair representation of the world's population of these once nearly extinct birds.

Finally, after days of unremitting gale, the wind has dropped. We take advantage of the stillness to hike up the canyon, following the Lake Louise trail along Torrey Creek. Ice is already sprouting in frozen fountains from the rocky slopes where the springs are freezing. Thick icicles, like a row of white dipped candles, suspend from a log fallen across the creek.

Higher up we come to the falls and find them transformed by the cold. In summer the black rock sides of the crevasse compress the creek into thunder, foam, and misty rainbows. Now the sheer rock walls are coated with a thick skin of ice. It sheathes the stones below and hangs from every outcropping like crystal draperies. The rainbows have been replaced with black and white.

Another mile and the trail levels out, winding through sloughs formed from seeping springs. These bogs have frozen too, the bright aspen leaves caught in the ice.

We are coming over a rise and starting to descend a dry slope when suddenly I catch sight of an untoward color above us.

"David," I say, and put out my hand.

Two orange-vested hunters are hunched on the ground high on the slope. Their attention is turned toward a bend in the creek below, a little pebbly beach sheltered on one

side by an overhanging rock and leading away into trees on
the other. A place where deer come down to drink.

The hunters have seen us now. We stare at one another
a bare moment. Then one of them waves us on. We feel
like civilians who have blundered into a combat zone.
Stupidly we stroll beneath their sights, making a show of
walking quietly so as not to startle their quarry. But our
stomachs are quivering. As soon as we're over the next hill
we stop and stare at one another. For the first time we
notice we're wearing dark green and brown and tan,
camouflage colors. All the horror stories of drunk and
incautious hunters come rushing to mind. We scan the
ledges above us, the coverts below. How many guns are out
there?

The sudden report of a rifle jars us. Something must
have stirred down by the creek. We force ourselves to go
on.

Another mile and we stop to drink our thermos of tea in
a field of half-buried boulders. The sky starts to spit snow.
Shall we go on? We're still nervous about the hunters. The
hike isn't a pleasure anymore but a polemic. Whose
mountains are these anyway? Why do you have to be armed
to feel like you have any business here? From fear of being
afraid we go on farther, dissatisfied.

At the head of another frozen slough I find the bleached
and bare pelvis of an elk. It must be several years old by
the looks of it. Tufts of orange lichen have already attached
themselves to the bone in patches. The spatulate ends of the
pelvis have been chewed away, either by coyotes or
chipmunks. These broken edges reveal the inner structure of
the bone and the secret of its surprising lightness. Inside,
the bone is not solid at all but honeycombed with air
spaces. It looks like stiffened meringue. I hold the pelvis up
to my face. The spaces where the muscles threaded through
make eyeholes in a mask. The spatulate ends are broad
horns. A good Halloween mask, we decide, worth lugging
home.

We turn back down the trail. It is getting too icy to go
on, and we've made our point for the day. We stop at the
boulder field where we drank our tea and look through the
binoculars over toward Arrow Mountain. We can see, miles
away across the creek canyon and above us on the side of

Arrow, the tiny figure of a man leading a horse. The horse is slipping on the ice there. At length they disappear into the trees. We turn back to our own trail.

An hour later we come to the place where the outfitter was clearing brush from the horse ford across the creek. There just crossing the creek are the man and horse we had seen on Arrow. It is strange to have watched them so far away and now to converge with them, to come to the end of the trail at the same moment they do.

The man is riding the horse now and has his rifle over the saddle horn. No luck, he tells us. Got within fifty feet of a ram but didn't get a shot. He spits to one side contemptuously, whether of his skill or his luck I don't know. "That's life," he says, and rides on.

There is a controversy in one of the local churches concerning Halloween this year. Some of the members question whether dressing up like goblins and witches is spiritually edifying for their children. There are mutterings about devil worship.

I remember Halloween as one of the grandest occasions of the year when I was a child. Some say Christmas is for children, but it's really Halloween that is a child's festival, at least in our age. On that night, fear, never far from a child's mind at any time, becomes delicious. Frightening shapes are faced. You take on the disguise of fright yourself—a mask, a sheet, plastic fangs—and enter the world of darkness to explore the scary. You go out into the night and the wind—it's always windy at Halloween—clutching your little brother's hand. Other spooks distill out of the darkness; you run and shriek together, drawn toward a modulated hysteria, fronting fears, touching the edges of terror.

All the necromancy associated with Halloween is the best thing about it. For one night of the year, darkness, death, the unknown, all these great fears of mankind are trotted out, caricatured, flirted with. We scare ourselves so we can laugh at our fears. Maybe it's not the most sublime statement to be made about death, but it is very human.

Most children today have no idea, of course, that the holiday that ends with gorging on sweets given as a bribe to neighborhood ghosts is actually the celebration of All

Hallow's Eve, the night before the Feast of All Saints who have died in the Lord. Before one can celebrate the dead in Christ, however, one must acknowledge that the saints are, quite plainly, dead.

Our celebration of Halloween began in the Middle Ages, when the Western world devised some of its most vivid reminders of death. Indeed, at times the age seemed obsessed with the fact; every day was Halloween. And not without reason. If the people of the Middle Ages were obsessed with death, it was because they were surrounded by it, steeped in it, soggy with it.

Life expectancy during those centuries was less even than in ancient times. No one could count on the biblical three score and ten as an actuarial age. In fact, of all the English kings, from William the Conqueror to the Tudors five centuries later, not one, not even those dying natural deaths, made it to seventy.

War, pillage, and siege siphoned off a good portion of the population. The Crusades, that marvelously macabre medieval invention that turned war into a pageant, went a long way toward invigorating the imagination about death. Raymond of Aguilers, chaplain to a French count, described the capture of Jerusalem in 1099 with eager detail: "In the streets and squares there were piles of heads and hands and feet.... They rode in blood up to the knees and the bits of the horses by the just and wonderful judgments of God." A Halloween scene in broad daylight.

But even more universal and inevitable than war was disease. Despite their contact with the advanced medical practices of the Arab physicians during the Crusades, the European doctors learned little from them. One appalled Arab medical man has left an account of a knight's leg being hacked off with a sword by his European physician—all to cure it of a boil that could easily have been poulticed. The patient died instantly as the marrow exploded from the splintered bone.

The land mass of Europe during the Middle Ages was a cesspool. The streets and rivers served as open sewers. Rats outnumbered the human inhabitants of cities. Plague bore down more implacably upon the European populations than it ever did over the recalcitrant Pharaoh and the Egyptians.

The Black Death first appeared in Europe at the port of

Messina in Sicily late in 1347. Within three years, Froissart, a contemporary historian, claimed that "a third of the world died." The death rate varied erratically. Bohemia was curiously immune to the infection. But elsewhere the plague took from one-fifth to nine-tenths and at times the entire population of cities, villages, monasteries. The sick died so quickly that corpses were piled untended in the streets. In many places there were not enough of the living left to bury the dead. The solitary survivors abandoned their ancestral villages, leaving them to desolation and decay. The Black Death broke out again during each of the next six decades, so that by the end of the century, Europe's population was reduced to half of what it had been in 1300.

Death was a constant, visible companion. The fertile medieval imagination was forced to devise powerful ways to confront and absorb the terror that stalked all classes, all ages.

It was the wealthy, of course, who had the means to solidify in stone these inventions of the imagination. They contracted with sculptors for elaborate tombs, hoping to live long enough to see them completed. The patrons as well as the artists knew that death comes suddenly and unexpectedly, and emphasized this point in all their funerary art.

An excellent example of this moral is found in the Book of Hours made for Mary of Burgundy and her husband Maximilian. The first illustrations in the book were done while Mary still lived. Before the book was completed, however, she had been killed in a hunting accident. One of the last plates in the book depicts the scene. It shows the couple out hunting on horseback. Mary herself is being pursued by three armed corpses, their shrouds flapping from their skeletal bodies. No one, obviously, expected the painful scene of Mary's death to be omitted from the book or even softened.

The tombs of ecclesiastics and the nobility were topped with stone or metal effigies of their owners. Often, either human pride or fastidiousness prescribed that the body be shown at its fittest form and disposed in an attitude of recumbent prayer. But a good many contracts gave instructions for the tomb effigies to be rendered with all the grisly details of death. In the abbey church of Saint Denis, for example, lie the figures of Louis XII and his queen. The physical beauty of the statuary is enchanting. Their long, graceful hands are folded in prayer. Yet, as though to shock by contrast, both their bellies are shown slit and stitched together with the embalmer's thick thongs.

Some of the age's great seemed to want it both ways. On top of their sarcophagi the fully regaled effigy is shown with all the symbols of office and power, a scepter or a bishop's staff. But beneath, often visible only through tracery panels, lies the image of a detailed and decomposing corpse. The granddaughter of Chaucer, the duchess of Suffolk, is thus rendered, stretched out on her shroud, her long hair falling from her skull. At Tewkesbury the tomb of John Wakeman shows a mouse, snakes, and snails nibbling on the corpse. And René de Chalon left instructions that he should be depicted on his tomb "as he would be three years after his death." Even when the figure of the deceased is not shown in its decomposing state, death's grim aspect may otherwise be suggested. For example, the upright effigy of Maria Vilalobos in the Lisbon cathedral is reading a devotional book, but at her feet three small dogs are gnawing the bones of a chicken they have just killed.

It is difficult for us, across the chasm of five hundred years or more, to understand the implications of some of the medieval death provisions. Great personages dying far from home sometimes left orders that their bodies be dismembered, the flesh boiled from the bones, and the skeleton brought back to its native land for burial while the rest of the soupy remains were to be interred at the site of death. Perhaps it was only a health precaution. But Cardinal Lagrange provided in his will that his corpse be "boned" and the skeleton buried at Avignon while the flesh was to be taken to Amiens for interment, an act symbolic perhaps of his divided loyalties.

The scattering of ashes, so often desired by the deceased today, does not strike us as nearly so strange, unless, of course, one has undertaken such a task and been surprised at the little knucklebones and bone splinters left unconsumed among the ashes.

The centuries-long Halloween party we call the Middle Ages reached its climax toward the end of the period with the *danse macabre*, the Dance of Death. Its origin appears to have been a thirteenth-century poem, *Le Dit des trois morts et de trois vifs,* which relates how three young and healthy hunters in the prime of life come upon three corpses in the woods, corpses they recognize as their own. The story so gripped the popular imagination that paintings depicting it were commonly rendered on the walls of churches from Italy to England to Denmark. Holbein illustrated it; Villon used it as a theme in his own poems. A great wall painting showing the corpses taking by the hand their unwilling living counterparts from all classes and stations of society decorated the cloister of the Holy Innocents in Paris. Below it were rows of charnel houses holding exposed bones. "Advance, see yourselves in us, dead, naked, rotten, and stinking. So you will be," the caption of the painting warns.

This gruesome, bone-filled cloister, unlikely as it may seem to us, was a popular spot for romantic assignations of the day. Perhaps the intended message went astray and the illustration was interpreted to mean "Eat, drink, and be merry, for tomorrow you die." In any event, it was the liveliest place in Paris. Not only did prostitutes solicit there, but shopping stalls sprung up within the cloister itself. Death was so familiar as to be almost cozy.

The *danse macabre* was actually performed as a masque in the fifteenth century both in Paris and Bruges, with people dressing up as corpses from various stations of life, from beggar to king. Death's impartiality was of ponderous significance in the Middle Ages. In a society structured by hierarchy, death was the one democratic statement. The grave was the ultimate leveler against which even monarchs and prelates were powerless.

The modern imagination recoils from these gory tomb effigies and strange burials and dancing with skeletons, just as, no doubt, the medieval imagination would find our trick-or-treating a tepid and inadequate means of confronting so basic a terror. We lack their tough realism about death. Our taste tends toward sympathy-card sentiments and floral tributes.

Still, if we look more closely at our own artifacts, I think we could match the Middle Ages horror for horror. We say their pervasive morbidity was caused by the Black Death and feudal wars. What about our Bomb and the icons of the holocaust and Hiroshima? If the paintings of Breughel are criticized today as excessively gruesome, would we care to put our photographs of Auschwitz up against them? Or the exhibits, casually displayed in shopping malls, of nuclear disaster with their pictures of dissolved flesh sliding from skulls, exposing eyeballs and jaws?

There can be no serious civilization that is not absorbed with the details of death. All mortal flesh is necessarily fascinated by its fate. The cardinal who had himself boned is not much different from the organ donor of today. Both kinds of behavior are products of a culture's imaginings about death. Organ banks and liver transplants are no less visually grotesque than any other kind of dismembering, especially when photographed by *Life* magazine. The insertion of a living but disembodied heart or kidney into a foster body is, imaginatively, quite bizarre.

We like to think of our modern sensibilities as properly hygienic and healthy; we concentrate on slick artery walls and straight teeth. We keep no skulls sitting around on our desks to contemplate our mortality. We are life-oriented, we say, and find that morally superior to morbidity.

But we have our own ways of inventing Halloween. We have made the metaphor of growth, for instance—economic, intellectual, spiritual growth—the object of our unqualified desire. But consider the visual content of our metaphor. Is not growth without limits, without restraint, the definition of cancer, a cell that keeps on reproducing itself? And cancer is our own age's Black Death.

Perhaps the sexual solicitations among the charnel houses and the *danse macabre* were defense mechanisms for an age that had to bear the unbearable, their own fear of extermination. Are our own fears any less?

Sometimes my astonishment at human stamina almost matches my despair of human frailty. All the centuries of death, the piecemeal loss of everything and everyone we love—how have we borne it all? How *do* we bear it? I go to funerals and look at the faces, wondering. How do they bear it? What have they done with their grief and terror? Maybe we swallowed it long ago with our Halloween candy.

All Hallow's Eve
After church we take off for Togwotee Pass, heading northwest toward the Tetons. Along the Wind River, where

it loops back and forth across the valley floor, the willow flats are a mixture of red rust and magenta. The colors of the earth have changed irrevocably now. They are the heavy, somber colors of winter.

In the Tetons the hunting season ends today. Coming down the pass toward us is a steady stream of hunters. These folks are headed home now, across the state to Casper, or back to Nebraska or Minnesota.

As we climb we cross the snow line. A foot of snow lies in the tucks and cracks of the slopes and hangs drooping on the trees. The cold, with its steady, simple, severe loveliness, has come to the mountains.

We climb higher and ice begins to encase the roadway. A ridge of snow half a foot high marks the edge of the pavement where the plow has passed. Pickups caked with mud and ice, trailers full of packhorses and hay, four-wheel-drive vans, and one-ton pickups pour down the pass. We are practically the only vehicle headed up. It's over, I think. At least for this part of the mountains. The elk and the moose can ease back into their habitat here.

Suddenly, the right wheels of the car catch in the plowed snowbank. "Not so close," I shout. But it's too late. We're in, sliding, the snow pulling us down and sideways into the ditch. The car finally stops, several feet from the upright pole of the snow marker just ahead.

On our left the heavy homebound traffic continues droning by. David reverses hard. No good. The tires only slide sideways and farther down into the ditch. He climbs out on the high side, walks around to the rear, gestures for me to steer while he pushes. The sky is a heavy blue-gray behind him. We are in no real danger unless there should be an unexpected skid by a vehicle in the descending lane. We have slid off against the mountain side of the highway, not on the precipice side. We're not going over an edge. Yet I can see David is fighting panic.

A small car stops across the highway. A young couple cross the road to us. "Need any help?" they ask. Their faces are exceptionally handsome. He is fair, she dark. He wears a cowboy hat and elegant fur-lined white leather gloves. She has on ski mittens. They are as perfect and simple as the snow.

David has pulled a shovel from the trunk. Together the

three of them dig and push, dig and push. David is frantic
and talking unnaturally. I smile and nod stupidly from the
driver's seat.

A pickup stops across the highway behind the car.
David considers the tow chain he has stored in the truck for
emergencies but decides to try one last heave. They lean; I
gun the motor in reverse. The car slides. Then, suddenly,
we're out. He stands in the middle of the highway and
thanks them. They say good-by. He climbs in the driver's
seat again and eases forward.

He is clutching for breath, for calm. He rummages in
his pockets for medicine, gives two shots from each aspirator
into his lungs. Another mile. I can see the thudding pulse
slacken in his throat. I watch the road, the snow, him, from
the corner of my eye.

Gradually, the world slows down again. I realize I have
gripped the wheel so tightly with my left arm that the
muscles are knotted and sore. I still see him against the
snow, down on his knees digging in short, rapid jabs, his
mouth open for air and anger.

On the Teton side of the summit we stop at the lodge
for coffee. Nothing is said of the terror, neither his of some
irreversible calamity coming upon us unawares on a Sunday
afternoon, nor of mine that he would collapse in the snow. I
think of Moses again. "At an inn on the way, I AM met him
and sought to kill him."

We listen to the conversations of the tourists around us.
One table of hunters, twenty years older than we are, with a
guide twenty years younger, discuss the vagaries of the
airfare each paid to fly from the East Coast to Wyoming.
People are always surprised at how hard it is to get to
Wyoming from anywhere. The hunters swear a lot and their
profanity is wearing.

We pay the bill and David asks the manager about
cross-country skiing at the lodge. But halfway through the
conversation he stumbles and swallows the words, overcome
by a sudden incoherence. Another customer interrupts to ask
for the telephone, and we slip out the door into the snow
again. In the parking lot the snow is spotted here and there
with dull blood. Scraps of coarse elk hair are caught in the
packed ice.

We edge back up to the summit of the pass where an

overlook, certified by the National Organization of Garden Clubs as "one of the most beautiful places in America," faces west toward the Tetons. Their improbable peaks are covered this afternoon with dark clouds, but their feet are lit with a bright striation of sunlight.

We leave the car and set off across a slope, slogging in our boots through the snow. The silence is as palpable as the snow. We enter it like a sanctuary. And here, in this place, the terror dies at last and completely. For we are suddenly in another world, another kingdom. The terror is taken up into the purity of this place. This huge expanse of white, these spruce embedded like spears in the sky, have, ever since they came into being, never deviated from their exact intent. They are free from the freedom to do so. It is this purity of being, uncalculated, unchosen, that arrests our attention. This is what we have been looking for, what we ourselves would look like if we could only mind our own business, stick to our own vocations as well as the trees do.

The surface of the snow looks grainy because of the minute shadows cast by fresh fallen flakes. Across this blue-shadowed background loops a hare's long tracks, leaving indentions in the snow, pressing smooth the grainy texture, so that the tracks look as though a light were shining through them. The world lies about us even and sloped in clement curves. We cross a rail fence and enter the trees. There the quiet clicks against the ear, in the blood. Quiet so austere it snaps. Little ledges of light snow lie along dry twigs level with my eye; scraps of gray-green moss feather from them. The dark and the light are perfectly balanced in the silence. We stand, pulling the silence into us, pulling it into our lungs and then our blood, eating it with every orifice in our heads.

There are moments when death would not be unwelcome. There are places so perfect in purity that one's dissolution there would be the only fitting act. Any movement, even a thought, would mar the perfection. To go on from here would be inelegant.

But after an hour we climb back in the car, feeling the moment already slipped, knowing the purity has been left behind in the silence, outside ourselves, perhaps even inimical to ourselves. We knock the snow off our boots, take off our caps and mittens. Put the car in gear. Start the descent. Fall in line with the hunting rigs.

At the bottom of the pass, back in town, the streets are lined with rigs, the restaurants full of hungry, grubby hunters. At the locker plant, a row of deer and elk hang head down, their bellies slit and vacant. This is what waits when you live to come back down the mountain, whether you're carrying tablets of stone or only the memory of trees and snow.

November

Three nights ago I happened to be sitting by the window, watching as the moon rose full over the east ridge. Through the binoculars it looked like a huge bubble just rising clear of a dark wave. The bare limbs of a dead tree on the rim of the ridge were silhouetted against its bright disk. I expected a coyote to raise its long head and howl. The moon's body, brighter than silver even, has the peculiar beauty of reflected light. You can look at the moon directly and not burn holes in your retinas. A cold sort of beauty, perhaps, but one that calls forth cries from a great many creatures. Coyotes, owls, cats. And myself. Oh, I say, as the enormous ball, like a thin shell of a sphere, like a scraped skull, finally floats clear of the earth.

The next day there were geese on Ring Lake. Canada geese, with the white chin straps that make them look like wimpled nuns. I hear them call, and I think at first it is a pack of dogs yelping somewhere down the canyon. In the bright, windy afternoon we go out to watch them—over a hundred—paddling at the north end of the lake.

Ring Lake is freezing. A thin sheet of ice has spread

over about a third of its surface. Being shallower than either Torrey or Trail Lake and facing head-on into the north wind, it freezes first. In fact, the inlet from the creek where David most often fishes is frozen nearly across. We see a gaggle of geese, six or so, promenading on the ice out near the middle of the lake.

Canada geese always return to their ancestral nesting grounds, which are a good deal farther north than Wyoming. And the young have only this one trip to learn the way home. Will they remember this stopover on Ring Lake? Will they carry it away with them, locked in their geese brains, up into the air over the Rockies, up toward the polar night? Will they be back next year?

There is another sound besides the geese. The ice itself, as we hunker in a protected cove, grates and scrapes against itself as the wind rocks the water under it. It makes a high-pitched sound, like stressed porcelain squeaking and chinking. Along the rocks at the shore, white shards the size of my hand have piled on top of one another where the edge of the ice sheet has grated against the embankment.

We follow a horse trail away from the lake across the sagebrush flat. Here one sees an opposite characteristic of the cold. Whereas the water expands as it freezes and breaks off its edges that push against the lake shore, the soil shrinks. Each rock and pebble sits in an island of space. The earth has drawn back from them, sometimes as much as half an inch. The stones and the ground contract with the cold, recoil from one another. The earth is shrinking. A cold void opens up between all its parts.

Yesterday, during the early morning hours while it was still dark, duck hunters crept into the campground on the other side of the creek. They left decoys floating at the inlet from the creek into Ring Lake. I heard them shoot at midmorning and the geese rose in a huge flurry.

Then before dawn this morning the hunters came back again. Their truck lights woke me, shining in the cabin window as they came down the hill and turned into the campground. Later we saw one of them out in a canoe on the lake. The wind was very high. And when I came out of the cabin and started up the road, there was another one climbing over our locked gate with his gun and his dog.

In the afternoon we drove down country to Riverton. It was like moving two weeks back in weather. The trees there, seventy-five miles to the south, still had some leaves left. But the colors were muted along the Wind Valley as we climbed back in the last light. The bare cottonwood branches were the color of old hair-combings.

Today, in the late afternoon, I take a walk around the east side of the lake. All day the skies have been heavy, the wind blowing hard. On the southeast edge of the lake lies ice debris left from the past two day's thawing. The rim of ice that remains, still stretching thirty feet out from the shore, is crazed and cracked. On its surface are chunks thrown up by the wind and the rocking of the water. In place of the clear, clean, glassy sheet, there is now just a slovenly clutter. Rubbled ice littered with leaves, twigs, and all the dead things that fall, eventually, into the water.

The lake has changed color with the sky. The fringes of the waves are not white as on sunny days, but dull pewter. The water echoes the gray-green of the sagebrush. The fir, the pine, the spruce maintain their shades of green, but the junipers are growing rusty, waning toward russet and ochre on the edges. Their loss of green looks like a loss of hope. But then junipers are not lofty trees. They keep their heads down and hug the ground.

I round the corner from the peninsula and start up the east trail around the lake. An untidy snow is beginning to fall. The flakes are large and gray, straggling like unconsumed ashes from some chimney. Ashes, ashes, all fall down.

The trail rises slightly above the lake here. I watch the narrow path between the sagebrush for tracks. Deer, coyote, sometimes a cat pad. And then suddenly there is a bush blooming with feathers and white down, caught and trailing from the twigs and tridentine leaves. Someone has shot a goose.

The trail and brush for twenty feet are littered with the leavings. Feathers a foot long and dark brown, their hollow quills opaquely white. Five-inch feathers, ridged in perfect logarithmic curves, a poignant taupe. And all shades in between those two, until, finally, one comes to the down. Soft as dandelion fuzz and as weightless. It is spilled everywhere, clings to everything. A white and buoyant efflorescence, unexpectedly blooming on the jagged, peeled stalks of sage and the rocks.

The carcass, of course, is gone. There is only one spot of blood on a feather I pick up. Someone has gotten his goose for the season. Canada will be one short this year. The litter on the hillside is all that is left of that life. The littered lake, the littered sky, the littered hill. The world seems full of disorder and death today. The pieces aren't fitting together. Well, the mind works like that. It doesn't need news of Central American coups or starvation in the Sahel to despair. A dead goose will do. Or sometimes just dead aspen leaves caught in the dirty ice.

In the afternoon while the wind is still, we go out to check the pump on the water system. A concrete pipe three feet in diameter is sunk in the bank of the creek with a tarp thrown over its wooden cover and rocks piled on top to weight it down. Inside all this is the pump. We roll the rocks from the tarp and tug it off. I step back as I see snakeskins, a score or more, wrapped around the housing. The sloughed skins are palely yellow and translucent. Is this a tribal serpent sloughing ground, or does it represent several generations of the same snakes? Alongside the skins lies a small gray mouse with a white belly, slightly deflated and flattened on one side.

Inside the pump housing, the air is warm. The heater, put there to keep the pump from freezing, is working. We cover it up again, disturbing neither the snakeskins nor the mouse.

This morning a fine snow is falling. The trees on the ridge are fully flocked with it. The road, where no one has passed yet, is a white band across the hill's brown face. And the width of the ice on the lake is easy to measure as the snow collects on it, bright and white against the dark water.

In the afternoon friends come to visit. We walk them upstream along the creek to see the beaver building his dam. He hears us coming and disappears. We watch the west ridge above the cliffs for bighorn sheep, but see none. The creatures aren't displaying themselves today. So we look at the Indian petroglyphs on the rock faces instead and then come in and build a fire.

Our cabin is stuffed with bodies, six around the table for supper. I make everyone sit so that I can shuttle the dishes from the stove. There is talk and laughing and music on the stereo. Human sounds. The cat sleeps on her pillow, nonchalant.

When they are gone, we walk up to Trail Lake in the dark. David wants to check the fishing line he left there. He drops down to the lake shore while I keep to the trail along the cliffs. The darkness is very close; with the clouds there are no stars to lift the sky tonight and the blackness presses down into the canyon.

I had thought I would be able to follow the trail without a flashlight. Usually its chalky line shows up white even in the dark. But tonight even its dim reflected glow is gone. Suddenly I am beset by fears. I know there are rabbit and badger holes a foot wide along this path. I could break my leg falling in one. And rocks as big as cats lurch out of the ground. I could stumble. In this darkness I could wander off the trail altogether. Something I have not felt for

years, stark fear of the dark, comes over me. I cannot see
where I am going, where I am. A blind abyss made of
blackness presses against me. I come to a standstill, afraid to
go further.

Down below I see the silver gleam of the lake. A duck
calls, complaining. All I can do is stand in the dark and
wait.

When finally the bright flower of the flashlight moves
toward me along the trail, its petals spread like a star. I
stand stock still in its path, staring like a wild animal,
wondering if my eyes reflect its unnatural light as theirs do.

The flashlight makes a weak pool of yellow light on the
ground, but it is enough to show me where I am. Only this
little bit of light in all this darkness and the fear is gone.

David holds up his stringer. On it is a fine fifteen-inch
trout. It is strange to think that while we were chattering in
the cabin, wiping our mouths in the light by the fire, the
fish was swimming through the dark water, striking the line,
taking the bait, waiting.

David opens the trout's mouth and shows me its row of
fine white teeth.

Quite, quite still today. Tidal waves of fog tumble down
the slopes, as though they had tripped and fallen over the
rim of the canyon. In the afternoon I hike up the east ridge,
cutting across the lateral moraines and clambering straight
up the rocky slope till I strike the trail.

This trail is my ossuary. I always find on it some long
tooth, some boomerang-shaped jaw bone, some vertebra
dropped there by death. These bones are always clean and
dry, well past the stage of decay. How this happens, I don't
know. Lewis Thomas mentions in one of his books the
wonder that, although creatures die by the scores regularly
out in the open, one rarely comes across their carcasses.
Not, certainly, in the numbers one would expect, except of
course on highways. Where *are* all the dead bird bodies, the
rabbit corpses, the prairie dog cadavers? Where is their
funeral parlor? Are the scavengers really that efficient? All I
ever find are these tidy little tokens, bits of bone, dry and
ornamental.

I stop often on the trail, both because it is steep and
because it offers varied perspectives. I can imagine myself

as a figure inside some medieval painting, appearing at
different places along a winding trail. The trail is the thread
that stitches events together. In medieval paintings, the
perspective comes from inside the picture, not from outside,
as in Renaissance paintings. I am looking out of such a
frame.

I look down on the inverted angles of the cabin roofs,
their mineraled paper covering a glowing gray. In winter the
colors of the cabins themselves get absorbed into the
background. The valley floor looks as faded as a long-
pressed leaf, as an old lady. The sagebrush seems grayer,
the earth more dun than ever. The conifers are almost black,
except for the junipers, jaundiced with russet. Further up
the canyon, however, in the willow flats broadened by
generations of beaver, there is magenta and puce among the
darker grays. These colors drag the eye toward them, the
only wealth on this impoverished palette.

I climb out on top of the ridge. It has become a seawall
today. An ocean of fog lies beyond it to the east, covering
the Wind River and its broad valley. The mist condenses to
ice crystals as it strikes the northeast side of the trees here
on top. They are all precisely half-flocked with freezing fog,
their backsides bare. I stand and watch the drifting fog as it
rolls up the ridge. I can hear the minute crystalline sounds
as it sifts into the fir needles.

Sometimes the breakers of fog draw back and the valley
opens and expands toward the east. I can almost see the
badlands, the highway; then it washes in again, the white
translucent wall of water vapor covering the valley like a
seafloor. In and out, in and out, like breathing. I might be
inside somebody's lungs.

I start back down the trail. The fog is following me
now, spilling over the seawall of the ridge. As I reach the
sagebrush flat again, inside our canyon bowl, huge spinning,
fast flakes of snow begin to fall.

Today Trail Lake has frozen over. It came as a shock to
me; I was stumbling down the hill in the absolute stillness
that has been upon us since yesterday's snow when I
discovered it lying like a body in my path. The trees were
immobile, stable against the sky. The dry spikes of grass did
not quiver so much as a millimeter. And below, the lake,

dark gray with only an afterthought of green in its depths, was as still as death. In only one night this body of water, slightly larger and much deeper than Ring Lake, had been sealed off under plate glass. Luckily, David had not left his fishing line in last night. It would have been stuck there all winter.

The lake froze like someone dying in his sleep, suddenly. Unlike Ring, dying by inches, freezing and thawing, throwing up ice-rubble along its edges, Trail Lake went quietly and quickly. The edges are as clear and glassy as the middle.

I stand on a promontory maybe twenty feet above the surface and peer into its rocky bed. From this angle and range, the water is quite green. I try to see a fish, some movement under the ice, but there is nothing except the absolute stillness.

David saw the otters again today. They were walking on the ice of Lily Pond and diving into the free water where the current runs through it.

Otherwise, all is still, still.

The wind has come back, doubly strong after the respite. We could hear small gravel rattling in the stovepipe this morning. At noon we put a quilt across the window where the wind got in despite the storm windows we have put up.

I didn't go out all day until almost dusk. The wind often slacks some then. I walked along the road by Trail Lake, rapidly to keep warm. The snow squalls that have swept through have left a white furred finish on its clear surface. In the last light the wind whirls the snow from the ice into high, huge shapes, spins them out across the center in ghostly arabesques. Like dust devils in the desert. The blown snow is like a dancer on an empty stage in some solitary, private performance.

As I come up on Trail Lake this morning, a strange new sound, almost like the calls and whistles of whales, stops me. Surely this must be some otter prank, some mad mammalian noise from under the ice. I creep forward, scanning the lake shore and the open water with my binoculars to take whatever it is by surprise. For a full fifteen minutes I crouch in the cold, straining toward the sounds, and trying to sort them out. Then it comes to me. The noise is nothing but the lake itself.

It may have gone to sleep peacefully, all in one night, but now, in later, deeper freezings, it has found a voice. The stress of varied temperatures, currents running, the air trapped beneath its thickening skin, has cracked its surface like crazed porcelain. Out on top, in the open air, these pieces grate against one another like arthritic bones cracking and popping. But the sound waves set up under water are from another world. They race across the lake, bounce back and forth, ricochet and echo. The noise is like that of a huge video-game arcade, a shoot-out with space guns, as the lake whoops and zooms and poings. I stand and watch in amazement, although there is not really much to see. Only the ice opaque now with blown snow.

Tonight I lie in bed and listen to the moaning of Ring Lake. It lacks the depth and resonance of Trail, but it startles us with an unearthly cry now and again. The lake, the living lake, trapped for the winter under the ice, cries out like a voice from the grave. Like something buried alive.

I look out at November in the evening light. This is what I see framed by my front window. The Absorakas gleam blue and white away to the northwest. The Ramshorn is striated with snow and rock. The western face of the Cathedral peaks is a sleek three-thousand-foot dune slope of sheer snow. Landscapes are incapable of irony. Mountains always mean exactly what they say.

In front of the mountains are the badlands, snow lying flat along the plateaus there. Then comes the inverted proscenium arch of the sloping canyon walls. The lake fills in the bottom of the V between the canyon walls. To someone sitting at the window, there first appears a strip of creek, then a strip of land, then a strip of lake, contained on both sides by the canyon walls and pointing like a wedge toward the Absorakas.

This near scape of land, right outside my door, is different both from the white, uplifted, self-sustaining solitude of the mountains and from the sloping, self-effacing canyon walls. Tall trees—fir, pine, and juniper—thrust upward from the peninsula of campground that separates the stream from the lake. Along the water's edge grows a mixture of thinleaf alder, water birch, and willows. Beneath these are the various grasses, all turned wheaten yellow. And of course in the near foreground the gray-green sagebrush. The boles of the bare deciduous waterside trees look like streaks of dried blood, while the twigs at their tops are the slightest orange. The standing dead snags among them are only gray.

So these are the colors. Intense midday light tends to wash the colors out; in any case they can't compete with the noon's cobalt sky. But in the last light they begin to glow. It is at this moment that they try to speak.

They are what we call muted colors. Gray, ochre, magenta, umber, dun, rust, deep dormant green. And it is with these muted mouths that they are trying to speak. They come right up to the window and with their combined and silent voices try to tell me something. I sit still and try to hear. This is the link with the earth that I wait for, for they are trying to tell me something about dying. But their only words are their colors. So as the night comes, with their last breath and at their most heightened moment, they say those colors to me, speak of themselves and of the long night that comes over them.

If I could learn to die as they do, well, there would be no problem. Still, even they do not simply put down their heads and go to sleep. The sap retreats, cell by cell. The branches writhe and lash themselves bare in the wind. The grasses dry slowly.

The world does not die in one day. It must live through its dying, moment by moment, day by day, week by week. But at each of those moments, days, weeks, more of its essential self, its skeleton, is revealed. One sees through the tree branches now to the far side of the creek. The grass and the split seedpods of the field flowers turn translucent. And we too. As we die, our skeleton emerges, the bare bones of ourselves on which the soft, corruptible flesh has lain. The fleeting, fatty tissue, the soft vulnerable organs, the gelatinous eyeball, even the long strings of muscle and tendon fall away.

What does my skull look like anyway? What is the shape of my junctured skull, the circumference of my joints? How is my pelvis placed, my backbone balanced? Only death will show this, my interior structure with its stuffing abstracted. I will be like a tree losing its leaves. And while I am dying, will I speak, like the land, with my own piercing, mute voice?

This morning—one of fierce wind—a weasel dashes out of the brush on the far side of the creek, plunges into the water, and comes out again, a fish flopping between his teeth. Away he goes again, into his burrow with it. The fish, I presume, did not have to fret itself about how to die. Death, like the Holy Ghost, simply came upon it.

This is the last day of hunting season for humans, but not for weasels. Nor for hawks, one of which settles down on a dead tree by the creek. He has spotted the weasel.

The fish, the weasel, and the hawk make up an equation to prove to me that hunting is natural. Human beings have long been the last factor in that formula. I could quote Isaiah about lions learning to eat straw like an ox when the world is finally redeemed from its futility and formulas, but then someone would quite rightly point out that eating anything involves death. The hay itself had to be nourished by the decay of other organic matter.

Of course, that is hay—and life—as we currently know it. We live in a world where life cannot be sustained without a corresponding death. No wonder when we try to conceptualize heaven, we end up making it a place of pure spirit. To do away with death, you have to do away with the physical world, at least as we know it now.

So why these elegiac complaints about the hunters for the past two months? What's the beef?

Just this: We are promised a new heaven and a new earth—not no earth at all. A new creation, not an obliterated one. I have faith in the Creator's ability, judging by his past performance, to regenerate a tragic world, to come up with one that can feed directly on his own life.

Nothing, so far as I know, *wants* to die, except here and there a human being. The fish tries to escape the weasel, the weasel evades the hawk. Yet none of us creatures escapes death and none escapes killing. It is our creaturely necessity and should remind us daily that we are not self-generating. We owe our lives.

It is the joy we take in killing that eludes me. Perhaps

it's only a matter of hormones. Perhaps hunters can't help their glee over a smoking bighorn sheep carcass, which they will never eat, any more than our cat can help her fascination with the mice she catches and plays with. Perhaps those hormones were necessary for survival at some point in our history. Without them we might have starved to death. Perhaps they only hang on like an outmoded appendix now. I hope this is so. I hate moralizing anyway.

But that doesn't stop me from groaning in travail with the rest of creation while I wait for all of us—the fish, the weasel, the hawk, and man—to be set free from our bondage to decay and for our bodies to be redeemed.

When we left for the airport before the sun was fully over the ridge this morning, the temperature was 17°. When I reached Denver at noon, it was 48°. They tell us on the airplane intercom over Kansas that the afternoon high in Atlanta, where I'm headed, is 56°. The world is thawing out as I head south and east.

So. Am I deserting death by taking this trip? Am I reneging on my own experiment? Am I really running wild-armed, out of the stoney sepulcher of Wyoming, winding sheet flapping behind me?

There are six days ahead of me. Six days packed with people. Already in the airplane there are more people than I see in a month in Wyoming. The cavity of the plane is in fact just as wide and several times longer than the church's sanctuary where we sit on Sunday.

Are people life? I am used to living with rocks now. Rocks, one person, and a cat. The cat sleeps most of the time. The person, as I do, practices dying. And the rocks just sit there. Nobody makes much noise. Only the wind and, at odd times, the lake. A friend whose husband was a sheepherder years ago on Colorado's western slopes told me how he instinctively used to move the lids about on his woodstove very, very quietly, so as not to disturb the lake of silence in which he was submerged alone all winter.

Now people are murmuring around me or else they have headphones stuck in their ears. The stewardess asks if I want a magazine, a drink, lunch. She orders me to put my seatback up straight. I am obedient and look to see if she's pleased. She doesn't notice. What's the point of people if no one notices?

A disembodied voice claiming to be the captain tells us to look to the left where we will see Wichita. All I can see is the wing and a patch of hazy sky. The voice also tells us that outside the window the temperature is −64°. Now that's cold, even for Wyoming, although with the wind chill factor, not unknown. A gale of 125 miles an hour is pushing us along, the voice says, and our plane is now two-and-a-half inches shorter than when we sat on the runway in Denver. What about me? Have I diminished too?

He tells us when we are passing over Springfield, Missouri, but says it's no good looking, as the sky is overcast—or undercast from our point of view.

Four rows ahead of me, two men with headphones dangling from their ears talk loudly across the aisle to one another. The woman in front of me has hair the color of water birch beside Torrey creek—brown and gold and magenta together. It curls in lively, crisp curls and reminds me of the purling turbulence of the creek water running over stones.

Just as we land in Atlanta the sun is going down. Something, something is here too from Wyoming. What is it? Something in the shape and color of the sunset. The elongated oval of the lit sky, pointed on each end, fish-shaped, falls away over the horizon. It is a trout, a brookie, the silver and gray skin peeled back to reveal that same inflamed pink of trout-flesh.

They are trying very hard here to make me live. Each vowel and inflection in their voices touches my skin and galvanizes me. I can't keep from tingling and twitching from the vibrations.

"What is your opinion," a student says. "What do you think?"

Opinion? I have no opinions. Think? Dead people don't think. How can I tell them that? And what does a twenty-year-old care about death anyway?

The whole time I am on this college campus I never see the school. The whole region is shrouded in fog for the entire four days. I go from one interior to another—the chapel, the cafeteria, the library—without ever seeing any buildings. I suspect it all of being nothing but movie sets consisting of interiors.

The last afternoon, my lectures and luncheons finally all behind me, I get to go for a walk. Now I can afford to look at the trees and the wet, layered leaves.

The trees are, of course, different from the ones in Wyoming. Hemlock is their evergreen here. And the maples still have their leaves. The maples! They glow in transfiguration. Wet as they are, they flame. What I want most, what I do not get, is to sit for an hour, only one hour, in contemplation of one of these maples. There are a couple I can glimpse from my bedroom window. I get to look at them for maybe thirty seconds at a time. That is how living people arrange their lives. Yet the maples are there all the time. Glowing in the fog and the small rain.

A student, a thin blond boy in khaki with a speech impediment and a hearing-aid, confesses his background of poverty like a crime. I tell him to count his blessings. My poor childhood is the best thing I have going for me.

He asks was I really poor, or just, you know ...

I say I once lived in a tin barn with a dirt floor. He is satisfied.

He is lovely and full of light and, I suspect, holiness. He is thin and pale, his fair hair and lashes as light as a breath. I could weep when I look at him, so gentle and so intense. Sometimes, he tells me, he senses the Spirit so strongly he must go downtown with just his guitar and Jesus. But he loves school. Since he is poor, he goes a year and then drops out a year to work and pay the school for the previous year. He quakes as he talks to me. His name is David, and he trembles between abnegation and energy. He tells me he is often ashamed of being poor. I tell him, always be poor. Always.

Oh, David, I pray that this fog-shrouded hill, thrust up out of the Appalachian plain, will receive your sanctity, your simplicity, with humility. You are like the Virgin, lowly and nimbused with light.

There are others, of course, who don't come with their life in their hands, as though it were some strange, rare object that had suddenly fallen from the sky. They're a good deal easier to encounter. For one thing, they don't ever-lastingly ask for my opinion. One fellow brings his Bible to an evening lecture and reads it to me afterward. He has an earring in one ear, and I have hopes there is more of Hazel Motes in him than Jerry Falwell.

My student hostess comes to get me in the dawn fog to take me to the airport. Down on the plain the fog thins, and I can see the reaching arms of the bare trees branching into a tracery of twigs along the highway. She tells me she longs to go with me back to Wyoming, someplace where she doesn't have to curl her eyelashes.

All the people. They are so rich and various. Little do they suspect I am sucking on their marrow today. They can't escape me. I've carried them away, whether they know it or not, their literary Lothario.

And, at the Atlanta airport, I finally get the maples too. I take the train, the one with the computer voice that tells you when to get on and off, to the front of the terminal. There a row of maples, incandescent like candles in the rain, line the sidewalk outside. I stand and stare, forgetting my plans, forgetting my plane. The people hurry past. I don't blame them. How could you bear to live with such beauty if you didn't ignore it? You'd do nothing all day but gawk.

Later, in the air over northwest Arkansas, I pray for the fog-wrapped students I have left, treasures in a field, works of rich substance, like the troutish sunset and the maples.

Then I crane ahead for the mountains, trying to sort them out from the clouds.

Sunday night we drive down to the highway to meet our younger daughter at the turn-off. Finding your way up the canyon in the dark can be difficult, so David drives her car back over the riverbed road. She has come to be with us over the Thanksgiving holiday. What astounds her most is the darkness.

"It really is black," she says as she gets out at the cabin.

"Yes," her father replies. "We call this 'night.'"

She hasn't seen night for a long time. She looks down from her eleventh-floor dormitory window in Laramie on a world illuminated by building lights, parking lot lights, street lights, storefront lights. It's hard to see the stars for the lesser lights.

We say compline before we go to bed. She giggles as we start to sing the Nunc Dimittis, which somehow the two of us never begin on the same note.

"It's funny to think of. You two, sitting out here in the middle of the boonies, singing away."

It's true. It is funny. Our singing is strange and disjunctive enough to make us laugh. So why is the coyote's song fitting and expected?

Yesterday my daughter and I walked out onto the frozen lake. Although snow is beginning to collect on the surface and crust it, there are still places where it is clear and we can see all the way to the rocky bottom. She kneels down on the ice to look in. "It's like looking into a shop window at a jewel display," she says, "and the frozen bubbles of air are the stones."

We listen to the lake, which is noisier than ever. As it freezes deeper and deeper, however, the underwater sounds have less access to the open air. Only once in a while now does it still sound like a video game. It is more like the rumblings of an unquiet stomach.

This morning it is very cold. Five below. No wind at all. My theory is that the wind has frozen too. In my work cabin the ink has to be warmed before it will flow out the tip of the pen.

Now I have time to reflect on my trip, five days out of the Wyoming wilderness. There's no denying that it has caused a reversal of rhythms. It has taken three days to put away all the insistence of life again. Even its good intentions. Because intention is the opposite of dying.

The fir tree outside my window has no intentions now in winter. All its intent has sunk with its sap to its toes, deep underground. And the dead limberpine beside it, gray and gaunt, has not even intentions in its toes. After it falls it will gradually be grated down to humus by weather, become the ground for some other being. That is what we have to be prepared for when we die in Christ, when we give our lives up to God. The disintegration of the structures of our self-madeness. All our ideas of what we are. Our intentions. They must be ground to humus to become the substance of another intent. Humus is the root for humility.

The progress of my self toward death was interrupted for a week. For a week, I drew up sap again, against nature, reversing the flow, and gathered to me intentions. The progress toward humus was arrested. And now I have to practice once more relaxing the vesicles down which

intention trickles to the toes. There is a certain amount of
pain that accompanies these kinds of vacillating dilations and
contractions. It is easier to turn loose and stay loose than to
keep on clenching and releasing. Taut muscles, headaches,
and interminable internal conversations come from intentions.

I sit here in my work cabin, with the woodstove door
open, watching the fire. Yesterday we drove across the
meadow, now frozen iron-hard, and brought in the wood
from the dead trees that David cut over a month ago. It is
part of one of these dead trees that is burning in my stove
this morning. The trunk was so knotted and twisted that the
chunks split in crazy shapes and are full of pitch. They burn
very hot, and we are careful not to throw more than one
pitchy piece on the fire at a time or the stove might
explode. The resin runs out the end cuts of the wood,
exuding from the expanding, cracked capillaries. It looks like
the foam that forms on the top of boiling jelly or candy, and
I suppose it is, in fact, another form of boiling sugar.
This from a tree that has been standing, dead, for years.
The other sticks in the stove, dry, smooth, and palely
yellow, burn quiet and steady. But the pitchy knots spit and
pop with small erratic explosions. Black smoke runnels
around their sides and up the stovepipe, smelling sharp and
tarry, the way molasses tastes.
I close the stove door for a minute to increase the draft,
and the knotted wood inside begins to hiss and whistle.
When I open the door again, the stove's interior is engulfed
in flames. Gases are shooting from the knots as though from
acetylene nozzles. The straight-grained sticks are burning to
a fine white ash. The half-spent pitch coats the inside of the
stove with a furring of carbon soot. The sticks are giving up
their respective ghosts. Even among trees, there are different
ways of dying.
Tomorrow my daughter goes back to school. The short
holiday is over. She will be driving a '65 Dodge three
hundred miles, at first along the Wind River, then skirting
the eastern face of the Rockies, crossing the high Red
Desert, until the road empties onto the broad current of
Interstate 80. She goes back to noise bracketed between
twelve-story concrete walls rising like an anomaly out of the
Wyoming plains. She leaves behind the stillness of the

frozen wilderness. I make cookies for her to take back, but I cannot put the quiet into a box for her, nor the still lavender sky at dusk, nor the rabbit tracks in the fresh skiff of snow.

She goes back into chaos while I sit in the heart of calm. And there is nothing I can do about it. She goes back to that peculiar intensity of student life where one's awareness of making choices is heightened. At twenty, one rushes toward the future, honed to an edge and intent. But the blade inevitably breaks. If not entirely in two, then at least it is nicked and dulled. Only those capable of the most enormous sacrifice, that is to say, saints, are able to retain the fine, sharp edge. Francis, for example, who as a young man took off his clothes and never looked back. Teresa who lusted single-mindedly for Christ.

Do I want sainthood for my daughter? What parent could? You may as well ask if I'd take her to an altar on the top of Arrow Mountain with the sticks in her backpack for her own immolation. And at twenty she's already too old for sainthood anyway. She'll go the long way round like the rest of us. Around through intention, desire, ambition, achievement—and the shadow side of each. Through human closeness and its cloying. Through weariness and defeat.

And I can do nothing but sit and watch. Watch as in "keep vigil."

For over twenty years a part of my life was devoted to doing something. To protecting, guiding, nurturing, building the beginnings of a human edifice. Now there is no longer anything I can do. I pack up the cookies, an already defeated talisman, knowing they'll be crumbs before they ever reach their destination. I can offer my daughter no protection. A corpse has, after all, nothing to give.

I have never been so conscious of my inadequacy. Lean on me and I give way, collapse into a pile of bones. Ask my advice, I can only shrug my skeletal shoulders and stare. I cannot protect you, lamb. I cannot even temper the wind to your shorn condition. Life is bigger than both of us. *Vaya con dios.*

This is yet another lesson in what it is to die. To send your lamb, the fruit of your womb, out into the Red Desert alone. To send her into a world that will devour her if it can and spit the bones out at your feet. To give her up to a

God who is consuming flame and intends—I know he intends it—to burn the tarry pitch from her bones.

The fire in my stove is almost all ashes now. The inside of the stove looks like a heavy snow has fallen over the gold and pulsing coals, so white are the ashes.

My own life is pitchy. It gives ground grudgingly. Why couldn't I have lived a straight-grained, saintly life, growing unwaveringly toward the sun like an arrow aimed at God, instead of the convoluted life of ambition aimed now in one direction, now another, twisted, clenched, knotted upon my own purpose? Then dying would be the simplest thing imaginable. An easy exhalation of sun stored inside the straight-sided cells. One would simply waft away into the air like Elijah. Instead, I shed my resinous, tight tears, squeeze them out like the hot bubbly pitch that smudges soot across whatever it touches. My life burns hot, hot, hot; refuses to give up easily. Even though I know we all go up to Moriah sooner or later and lay down, like a defeated hope, our lives.

First Sunday of Advent

Here we all are at church. The sanctuary has its Advent colors on. The paraments are purple, the priest is purple. The light shines from the chancel as though a giant coal lies glowing there. The advent wreath, pungent with evergreen, hangs suspended from the rafters like a crown. The sly face on an acolyte tilts upward till his long-wicked lighter catches the first candle in the wreath. Then he smiles with satisfaction, like a young cat, and slips back among his friends.

The Sunday School children all sing, surrounded on three sides by a stockade of teachers. It is a silly song, like Old MacDonald's Farm, each verse devoted to a different animal and accompanied by mimicking gestures. A modern bestiary of a song whose moral content is a good deal thinner than any medieval counterpart. Nevertheless, it serves the purpose. We all smile at the wiggling tail of the fish, the curled forepaws of the kangaroo, the swinging elephant trunk. The backup group, the teachers, tries to inspire the children by performing with embarrassing vigor. Depending on age and temperament, the children look either bemused, patient, or eager. A few clearly like to perform. The others, especially the younger ones, are only puzzled.

Later there is a drawing from a plastic bucket for "secret angels." Much confusion attends this task as several people have put in extra names for the same absentee members, often duplicating them, so that, after everyone has drawn, some slips are still left at the bottom of the bucket. The mathematical exchange becomes too complicated, and in the end the vicar takes the extra slips.

He begins the sermon by blowing a party horn to celebrate, he tells us, the church's new year which begins today. He blows it tentatively and explains quickly.

At long last, after the candles, after the animal song, after the secret angels and the party horn, we settle down to the Eucharist. Just as at home one might touch the forks and spoons on the table lightly, moving them a fraction of an inch across the cloth to test their familiar weight, so we turn to the accustomed place in the prayer book and run a forefinger over the page before beginning. We sink to the wine-colored kneelers with a sigh of relief. That's enough now, enough innovation for the first Sunday. Give us a break, a little comfort. Please don't make the bread Christmas cookies or turn the wine to wassail. Not yet. We're not ready. We've only just begun preparing.

It may be New Year's for the church. We may be getting a jump on the world. But it is still winter, still Wyoming. And there's nothing very new about us yet. Our bones creak as we edge off the seat onto our knees, doing our ridiculous liturgical exercises. It's going to be winter a long time yet. The blizzards still haven't come. Nor the false spring of January, nor the renewed wrath of the wind that follows it. We've still got a long way to go. We need to conserve our strength, devise a campaign to combat cabin fever. Let's not blow it all this first Sunday in Advent. There's three more to go and then Christmas itself, which begins to look like an implacable juggernaut bearing down on us. The worst is yet to come, when we will be called upon for superhuman feats of endurance, longsuffering, patience. Spare us, for a little while, this Christmas. Let it *only* be Advent still. The slow accretion of cells inside the dark winter womb.

But this, of course, is an adult's Advent. The children

are greedy for the holidays, cannot have enough of surprises
and sweets and newness. Horns are fine with them. The
unexpected blat makes them laugh rather than flinch. It is
only the grownups, "woe-weary and wetshod" like Piers
Plowman, who have to sidle into Advent, protecting the
open sores of our chilblains from even the small vibrations
set up by the horn blasts. Langland's hero "fared forth like
a losel" into the cold medieval landscape of King Wen-
ceslaus until he "waxed weary of this world and willed oft
to sleep." Like us.

When we come to communion, the children kneel first
at the rail. They catapult themselves toward the cup as it
comes round. The deaconess frowns and wipes the dribbles
with her napkin. Afterward come we losels. The chalice is
tipped deftly toward our lips. We sip it gingerly, as though
it were scalding coffee to keep us awake during the long
winter ahead, or else a medicine that stings our cold sores.
Either way, a strong necessity for our poor condition.

Yesterday we drove up into the badlands, those eroded
and striated pinnacles of sediment that extend from the
foothills like twisted toes. Nothing grows in the badlands.
There is only color—ivory, viridian, olive, ash, lead, violet,
garnet, terracotta, vermilion—horizontal stripes of pure color
convoluted by wind and water into grottoes, castles, knotted
spires, slag heaps. This is not a hospitable beauty, not trees
and cushions of pine needles and sweet, unexpected alpine
sprouts. Nevertheless the contrast of austerity and pure
mineral color intrigues the eye if not the heart. In summer
these canyons are the haunt of rattlesnakes and bighorn
sheep—whatever creature wants to hide. That's about all the
badlands offer, a labyrinth of negative space in which to
wander when being lost is irrelevant.

There, beauty is stripped down to the elements of color,
shape, light, and shadow. There is nothing else. Not a single
twig to hang a sentiment on. No associations. Only fantas-
tical architectural analogies.

I wish Tolkien could see it. He wrote to his son about
his own fascination with barrenness.

> Much though I love and admire little lanes and hedges
> and rustling trees and the soft rolling contours of a rich

champain, the thing that stirs me most and comes nearest to heart's satisfaction for me is space, and I would be willing to barter barrenness for it; indeed I think I like barrenness itself, whenever I have seen it. My heart still lingers among the high stony wastes among the moraines and mountain-wreckage, silent in spite of thin chill water. Intellectually and aesthetically, of course, man cannot live on bread alone, and if there was not bare rock and pathless sand and the unharvested sea, I should grow to hate all green things as a fungoid growth.

We stood in a stiff wind on a high mesa in the midst of these badlands and watched the dark, upright, symmetrical shadows shift in the runnels of color. To the west the tops of the foothills, furred with the most delicate vegetation where a single footfall can damage a decade of growth, looked smooth and soft, like the rounded back of a newborn, sparse-haired puppy. Clouds were driving up against the Wind River range before us, spilling over from the Tetons. Like a gigantic snow fence, or teeth, they caught the storm and held it there up high, protecting this valley and the village below.

The sheer neurological demands on top of the mesa were almost too much to bear. If there were only the badlands to consider, or only the fragile, furred foothills, or only the stupendous upthrust of one mountain range. But there were all of these at once and several mountain ranges with the sky assaulting their crests. One's head began to ache with the effort and the stomach grew queasy. Darwin said that after the age of thirty he couldn't look at "fine scenery" or pictures or listen to music without an attack of nausea. He would never survive the top of this mesa. We had to crawl down to the car, complaining of the sharp wind, to save our senses.

At night, with the moon waxing, I have a dream about a wasteland of snow. In the dream, it is Siberia. In the middle of the snowfield is an enclosure, palings made of human arms and legs reaching out of the ground into a pewter sky.

Yesterday David hiked all the way to Lake Louise, and all he saw in the way of wildlife were some brook trout dashing around the free water in Torrey Creek.

I walked around Lily Pond and saw the beavers

hunched over their saplings, gnawing away. They whittled the sticks down to size, then wriggled under the ice shelf and swam to where their construction site barely showed above the frozen stream. I went a little farther on and startled two deer coming down to the creek for their evening drink. They run for a ways, then bound, stiff-legged, like birds or hares. Their ears are as long as rabbits' and their tails show white against their longer winter coats. When they reached the next dry knob over from me, they stopped and looked back curiously. Their camouflage is excellent. They are, this time of year, the absolute color of the earth. A muckled granite gray. When they had had all they wanted of me, they bounded away again, springing in easy stages over the moraine.

All the animals are cryptic here. They are designed so as to avoid detection. One almost has to know they are there in order to see them. No one is ever gaudy here, except a few male birds—mallards, mountain bluebirds, violet-green swallows—and then only in summer. In winter these scraps of color either migrate to flashier climes or change their colors to something suitably subdued.

Here is another lesson in death I am trying to learn from this land. How to hide. When the earth prepares for winter, when it dies, it becomes cryptic, withdraws more of itself from view. The vegetation effaces itself and, except for the evergreens, becomes the color of the ground at its back. Fades. And the animals, at further remove, must do the same. Become indistinguishable from their background. They return to dust, not just when they die, but every winter. They sink, visually, into the earth.

I stand here, upright, on the hillside. My boots and jeans are unremarkable enough, but I have a jacket on, a fuschia pink jacket, easily picked out in the snow or shadows, and a hat made of the brightest scraps of yarn in my basket. I am hardly cryptic. I'm not even reticent. I stand here, stock-still, and shout my colors in every direction: Here I am! Come and get me! Alive and glowing with synthetic dye.

Hiddenness, the capacity to drop below the threshold of visibility, has always been one of the great goals in most traditions of spirituality. The psalms echo with calls for the Lord to hide the singer. The apostle tells us our true lives are hidden with Christ in God, like the deer hidden among the hills. And when you get right down to it, invisibility is an attribute of matter itself. The whole world hides itself in electrons and energy fields.

Perhaps invisibility is actually easier to practice in the city where the rivers of passing eyes seine out, unseen, the inconsequential. The discipline is harder here in the wilderness where eyes survive by seeing farther and seeing first. If I could learn to become invisible to a squirrel, cryptic to a Clark's nutcracker, a good deal of my task would be done.

December

The world is suddenly white. This morning's snow has covered the ground and fills the air so that even the east ridge and the west cliff have disappeared. We can only see as far as the creek in front and the fence in back of the cabin. This is a finer snow than any we have had before, perhaps because of the colder air aloft, although on our porch it is only 25°. No wind.

The weather makes a holiday for us. We stay in bed later than usual. Dawdle through our prayers and breakfast, both of which are punctuated with exclamations that begin with "Look!" David packs a lunch and leaves. I disregard the clock entirely.

At midafternoon I finish lunch and my day's work. The snow is still falling straight—no wind. Now is the time, I know, to make a break for it. This is the crest of the wave as far as the weather is concerned.

Coat, hat, mittens, scarf, snow boots. The struggle to swathe oneself against the cold is exhausting. Finally I am out, out into the day. I try to step in David's tracks to keep from marring the perfect planes of ice crystals. I go along the creek to the place above the bridge where, sure enough, the beaver sits, oblivious to the snow holiday, gnawing his sticks. A beaver's mentality must be very antlike. Nothing stops his gnawing. He is unimpressed by the flake-filled air. His work is impenetrable. When he finishes his sapling, he lumbers under the ice shelf that arches the stream to make his next deposit on the dam. I go along the trail by the petroglyphs where I stood, afraid of the dark, on the night that Trail Lake froze. In this pasture some people have heard voices. David does; but when I listen I only hear the snow chittering against my jacket. The upheaved cliff has caught the snow in white diagonals across its face. The trees are weighted with it. This is a solemn, intent beauty, its energy focused by the sharp edges of snow against the dark evergreens and the rock ledges. I feel lifted up, invigorated by such clarity, even though the sky is a curtain of crystals veiling the lake.

"All right, voices," I say. "Speak up. Today I'm not afraid." I feel strength brewing in me, but no voice answers. I swagger on through the snow.

David is in one of the abandoned cabins, reading over a small fire. We lie on the floor in the intensified snow-light. He is as white as a unicorn.

On the hill above us a deer lies down. Its ears are spread like dahlia petals, and it hears us even when we walk across the floor here below. It stands and nibbles, then lies down again in the snow.

It is after four now, and to have any more of the day we must go out at once into the still-falling snow. Down the hill to Trail Lake, around behind the moraines, through a deserted corral, clomping through the sagebrush blooming with snow. Over another ridge and down into a hollow full of firs spilled from the east ridge. An owl lives in the trees there, and now, in the dusk, he is calling fiercely. His calls are so insistent they almost sound like barking. A small kittenlike cry comes from somewhere among the mounded rocks, but whose voice it is we cannot tell.

Dark is coming fast now, the snow striking into our north-turned faces like the tiny milk teeth of the storm. Ice has sprouted on David's beard and eyebrows. It's hard to see.

We stumble slantwise across the moraines, sliding on rocks and tangled brush. In the last light we can barely make out the white, expansive sheet on Ring Lake. Dark trees mark its southern end, and beyond them, the cabin. I should have left a light on there to guide us home through the falling snow.

"Do you keep catching a light from the corner of your eye?" David asks. "One that isn't there when you try to look at it directly?"

No.

"It's first on one side and then the other."

I turn my head back and forth. I see no light and hear no voices.

We struggle on through the snow across the meadow. Stop. We peer through the violet and moving air at something that seems about to happen. Emergent possibilities hover in the snow-filled air around us. We go on slowly, like children who hate to come inside after a long day of play.

Well. The day is over. David starts up the fire again. I sweep the snow off the porch so it won't turn to skating ice by the morning. We eat the soup I left in the pot. I read aloud an account of Virginia Woolf's madness while David washes dishes and makes a cake.

Already it is time to say our prayers sitting by the stove. I recollect that I am thankful for the snow, that it is such a snow that one can be inside its falling; I am thankful for the deer and its delicacy. For a beauty beyond ourselves that draws us toward desire, toward its source.

It is, in its way, a day of perfection. I never hope to have a better on this earth. Was it, however, a day of death or one of life? Was I cheating at my own game? Reaching after, pursuing, running with my open Faust-mouth after the world, beauty, experience?

Somehow, no. It was not, until now by the stove, self-conscious. It was a day I never noticed myself enjoying until it was over and I recollected. My self was submerged in snow, buried in the ice-filled air.

Air with nothing in it, invisible air, clear skies, gives us the illusion of being on top of everything, the earth at our feet. But when the air we live in becomes visible, palpable, then we sense our selves buried, implanted in being, moving through creation contingently, the way a trout moves through the tow under the ice. Then we see we are not controlling life at all, but catching at its currents, riding on its back, becalmed in its incomprehensible depths.

Wind today. Fierce north winter wind. The snow stopped last night, and the barometer, which had sunk to new lows, began to rise. I wish we had gotten the storm windows on my work cabin by now. The wind comes in under the front door like a cold, licking tongue and reaches down the stovepipe to suck the heat up the flue.

On top of the west cliff the snow is blowing southward in clouds. I hope the road drifts closed. I like to hear the wind come up in the night. The world shakes and shudders under its ferocity. It has a voice I can hear.

Our friend Maggie told us of several people who have heard the voices by the petroglyphs. She was concerned about whether the voices David hears are happy or hostile. It seems that at least one person who camped in that pasture overnight felt that someone was trying to invade his tent.

Also, a nun who stayed here one winter by the lake—
one very hard winter—went out on the ice one night and
lay down to talk to the moon. She had been alone a long
time. She almost didn't get up again from that rendezvous.
It was bitter cold, and she was on the brink of sleeping on
in the icy moonlight.

I may have come here to die, but only in the most
hardheaded way. I don't intend to be seduced into death by
moonlight on the lake. Nor does David take his voices
personally. For one thing, he only hears them when he is
walking. When he stops, they stop. And they sound too far
away to make out any words. Besides, they are not talking
to him, he says, but to one another, like people in a camp.

Yesterday I spent in bed, feeling sick and finishing the
biography of Virginia Woolf. She too heard voices, at least
during her intermittent bouts with madness. Unfortunately,
they were the sort that urged her to throw herself out of
windows.

Lots of people hear voices, I suppose, although not
many admit it. Nor are the voices hostile, on the whole, in
the accounts I hear. Upon the death of a favorite uncle, my
mother heard voices. She was alone in the house, washing
dishes one morning, when it seemed there were children
out on the lawn laughing. She stopped and went out to
look, not once but several times, and could see nothing.
There was a certain unaffected glee in their noise, and it
had nothing particularly to do with her. In this they were
like David's voices; both were experiences of unsought
eavesdropping, as though the door to another time opened
just wide enough for them to hear something going on on
the other side, something not directly addressed to them.

Virginia Woolf's voices sought her out, however. She
dreaded their approach. It meant the deepest sink of her
insanity. They spoke directly to her and with malice. In the
end, having gone through at least four battles with them,
she escaped the only way she knew, into the waters of the
River Ouse. But did she escape them, or did they lure her
there, the very voices she was trying to silence forever?

Madness, of course, is not simply the purview of the
agnostic or the effete. Blake was perhaps the most notorious
madman of his century. He insisted upon his voices, two of

whom were Madame Guyon and St. Teresa who had also heard voices in their day. Fortunately for Teresa, however, this was not automatically a sign of insanity in her day. Thus, her enormous intensity was allowed to channel its force into the world's working, greatly to the benefit of that world. Even Blake, moving against the great tide of rationalism, brought a good deal of blessing to his age and ours. But again, neither Blake's nor Teresa's voices urged them to destroy themselves.

However, there is also William Cowper, he of "the fountain filled with blood, drawn from Emmanuel's veins." How many singers in their pews on Sunday morning realize they have on their tongues the words of a suicidal maniac? Like Virginia, he had recurrent attacks of insanity, sometimes lasting several years. He probably never fully recovered from the last onslaught thirteen years before his death. No doubt he made it out of St. Albans, an eighteenth-century lunatic asylum, only because his path was crossed by a sympathetic doctor, himself a poet. Thereafter, Cowper had to rely on the protection of friends in order to live in the world. He could not even marry, a solace that Virginia, as a woman, was allowed.

Madness, it seems, is one of those arrows outrageous fortune draws from its quiver and shoots indiscriminately at believers and infidels alike. It is the deplorable custom of the church today to at least hint and sometimes promise that conversion insures sanity. But there are too many examples otherwise to make this credible. A whole society of believers at Salem, for instance, were capable of taking leave of their collective senses temporarily, of listening to voices from a realm hostile to humanity, voices aimed at making them destroy themselves.

The list could be extended, who knows how long? There is Luther, throwing his inkpot at the apparition of the devil, his lapses into severe melancholia. C. S. Lewis's last days were darkened by assaults from demons of despair. For Luther and Lewis the only way to win over depression was death. The voices that visited them were not, obviously, Blake's beneficent angels.

So when one talks about death in Christ, about laying down one's life or falling into the ground like a grain of corn, one has to consider, straight on, this matter of self-destruction. Is the seed insane to give up its life? Is there really any difference between the corpse on the cross and the body weighted down by a stone in its coat pocket under the water of the River Ouse? Both were dead. Both, in a sense, suicides. Are sacrifice and suicide synonymous?

Suicide makes its own attempt to defy death, if only by saying this is the moment, this is where *I* choose to end it. It's like handing in your resignation before you can be fired; it provides a certain meager sense of autonomy.

But Jesus himself said, "No one takes my life from me; I lay it down." What is the difference? If there is one, I believe it lies in the place where one chooses to lay it down. You can say, "Into your hands I commend my spirit," or you can just drop it, abandon it, willfully, alongside the road, in a ditch, under the water. And perhaps those are the only two choices in the end. To surrender your will to another one or to tear it up in little pieces and scatter it, inconsequentially, to the winds.

Even so, I am not complacent about surrender or sacrifice as the easy way out. "Thy will be done" is an open invitation to a Destroyer. And there is no guarantee that the hand that wrecks one's own will, one's own program and plans for building a life, will suddenly turn to creating. No guarantee except the Destroyer's own word: "I kill and I make alive." What kind of word is that?

The last word, I guess. Unarguable. So, given the irrefutable fact of death, one may as well launch oneself toward it like a rocket and, aimed at its exact center, perhaps find a way through. We can hurl ourselves at God only through the needle's eye. If you want to claim your life as your own, then you better be a suicide, quick. That is the only autonomy left to you.

For if you want to linger over it, lovingly protecting its little hoard of identity, then there is a kind of death by diminution. The self is soon exhausted by living off its uncommitted capital. One's powers simply evaporate over a period of time. Life continues only through a kind of autocannibalism. If one refuses the sustenance of the sacraments, what else can one eat except one's own flesh? Or the flesh of one's neighbors?

This is true for us all, however sane. I think we simply see the effects more starkly among the mad. (And madness itself is only one, if a harsher one, of the many possible conditions of life.) Those who are sane and self-sufficient simply disguise their entropy a bit longer; wait, sensibly, for death to find them, while gnawing at the hoard of their own bones, rationing it out, making life last, however rancid, till the last.

But look at poor, mad Cowper, groping after lucidity certainly, but even more after half-imagined heights, like a fish dreams of a freer atmosphere above the light-refracting, sluggish element in which he moves, an atmosphere he knows he must die if he enters. And yet, even in madness, the fish gathers himself, compacts his powers and muscle fibers, and then—leaps! Aiming himself upward, into the eye of death.

Lift up your hearts, we are exhorted every Sunday.

And every Sunday comes back the idle promise: We lift them up unto the Lord. Up into the air, piercing the heavens. Up so high we get above ourselves, beyond our natural element. Our lungs burst. For mortals to venture toward transcendence is certain death. Suicide. To bring ourselves to it, our love of light must be dearer than our love of life itself. It is madness to leave behind our dull and torpid safety.

But the alternative is only a submarine existence, to imagine nothing to lift one's heart up to.

"I have been half in love with easeful Death," said Keats. This is the kind of death-lust that takes its revenge on life for not having been all it should, for being full of betrayals and harsh conditions. Suicides are not really killing themselves. They are killing the world. That must be a different kind of death than one that gives up life for love of the world.

When he was quite old and his sanity still tenuous, Cowper wrote an inscription for a newly planted windbreak around a cemetery.

> Which shall longest brave the sky,
> storm and frost? These oaks or I?
> Pass an age or two away
> I must moulder and decay,
> But the years that crumble me
> Shall invigorate the tree,
> Spread the branch, dilate its size,
> Lift its summit to the skies.

There is no vengefulness in that gentle voice that speaks so calmly of its own decay. He does not despise the way in which matters are disposed on earth. With the tree, he lifts up his heart toward the light.

Second Sunday in Advent

This day I had occasion to discover just how much my self and my sanity are linked to the land.

Through a series of circumstances, I came home from town late in the afternoon, my body a battlefield of bruised emotions. The muscles in my neck were so constricted from pent cries that they ached and I could hardly swallow. My stomach and shoulders were knots and gnarls. Blake, I am sure, was right—our bodies are only the visible parts of our souls. And anyone who looked could tell mine was in a sorry state.

I hurried into my outdoor clothes. If only, I thought, if only I can get outside, I can find a voice for this choking hurt. Out among the rocks I could cry like that Gerasene demoniac. If I didn't find release for this compression of muscle, gut, and lunged air soon, I would die—if not for lack of love, then for lack of light.

So I rushed out, staggered out more exactly, gasping in the cold wind blowing off the lake and coughing it out again.

Bent double, I crawled through the barbed-wire fence and went on, half running around the bend in the fence, down toward the inlet of the lake.

And there, quite suddenly, with the sweep of snow combed back from the lake's edge, it left me. Whatever anger or anguish had boiled within my veins like a lump of potassium dropped in water, it was gone now. Evaporated. Blown away on the wind that whipped across the snow. It was no longer even interesting.

For here, with the drifts piled high on the leeward side of the sagebrush, lay reality, unperturbed and unregarding. A reality far more sure and substantial than that of emotions and human causing. Those simply didn't matter. Not in the face of the truest lines I ever hope to witness. Lines made of water vapor condensed and cooled into crystalline structures and swept into curves and vortices true to the precise pressures of air and velocity. Lines to break your heart with their purity.

Which is, I suppose, what happened. My heart, overwrought with its woes, simply broke against the superior substance of a solider creation. Here was a scrap of the world being absolutely true to its design, to its own nature, possessing its soul in serenity. And my own roiling and moiling, the erratic electrical discharges from my raw and blistered nerves, was sucked out, pushed out, dissipated on the wind of this impeccable and overwhelming reality. Pride was pitiful beside it. Was less; was nonexistent. I would never miss it.

So I slogged on, through the sagebrush drifts. In one momentary turning, within a heart's beat, my attention was transformed from anguish to awe. I found a cove where the blown snow was shaped by the wind into an upturned boat, a ghost keel filled up with white and whittled away from windward. The small sage was buried up to its unpretentious efflorescence with snow, which then trailed away southward in knife edges of ice. Delicate, yet worn that way by the ferocity of the wind.

We know things—important things—we cannot say. I know what the snow, the sagebrush, the wind are telling me, though I cannot say it.

I go on, around the lake's eastern edge, past the place where we cut the dead trees down for firewood. On along the trail, littered now, days after the snowfall, with rabbit tracks, deer, coyote, mouse tracks. From where the trail rises slightly on the bank, I look down into the brambles and overhung coverts of wild things, their paths marked clearly like subtle but distinct embroidery. I am grateful for this sign of their secret life, more silent than, but still tangential with my own. Even to see this line of tracks, imagine the coyote trotting on the same cleared ground as I am setting foot on, links me to a life that runs deep and steady through the earth.

I come out on a small peninsula that juts into the lake and feel like I am standing at Land's End. All the snow is sharp here. The ground is like an arrowhead aimed north, straight into the wind. The wind is so fierce it sucks the snow from around the entire edge of boulders otherwise buried, leaving a ledge knee-high on the windward side so that I can walk clear around the rocks on slick exposed ice.

The lake ice itself is clear, and dark only because the

lake bottom is dark with stone and silt. Captured in the ice are air bubbles looking like the light nuggets in mirrors that disappear into reflected infinity. In places, whole clusters of these bubbles have blown into streaks inside the depths of the ice.

It is all so cold and firm and beautiful. One could, quite easily, lie down and die for the very love of it, hoping only to be frozen in forever like the air in the ice. Or if not forever, which is a measurement of no consequence compared with this still moment in time, then like the encased air, till spring, when it explodes from the ice again.

> He gives snow like wool;
>   he scatters hoarfrost like ashes.
> He casts forth his ice like morsels;
>   who can stand before his cold?

This is *his* cold, this ice *his* morsels. The kind of work that made the world. How can one honor it enough?

I walk back up onto the peninsula. There, stuck in its point like an enormous candle flame, is a bristling limberpine. The branches rise from its base clear up the length of its bole, upward, and then at the top, tend inward, like the tip of a tongue of flame. A cold and perfect Advent candle. At its base is a patch of bare ground. Bare, brown, damp, and undisturbed. Either blown or melted bare by the wind that buffets the flame of the tree. The tree, I sense, has raised itself up into this shape to bless the light, has already been blessing it before I came along. The pine stands here, night after night in this ice-bound sanctuary, a flame in the freezing air, steady even in the wind.

And the ground, bare and brown before it, is like an altar. There is a steadfastness in creation that far exceeds our own artifacts. It is our primary reality check; before it our turmoil is brushed aside. There, everything fits, everything works, design overrides chaos. Merely to be in its presence is to perceive a will beyond and more trustworthy than our own. To put one's attention to such a use heals and hallows it.

So I stand there. I give up and up and up. I desire to be Isaac, both surrendered and saved. To sacrifice my contrite heart, not even contrite anymore because contrition has already blown away with the wind, taken off to whatever conversion waits for it. To be only still and small and silent.

From the cabin yesterday afternoon we could see the canyon up toward Middle Mountain already shrouded with snow clouds.

We drove up to the trailhead where a large flock of bighorns grazed in the meadow, one good-sized ram herding them around. They looked at us and moved off a few yards. With studied unconcern I ambled up a few yards closer. With equal unconcern they shuffled off.

The snow was already beginning to fall then, *graupel,* the round balls of snow that look like bits of blown styrofoam. We started up the trail along the creek. The surface of the stream has frozen over, heaved up, been coated with a couple inches of snow, and then, in places, has caved in. You can look into the dark running stream through these collapsed trap doors of ice. In some places the edges of the hole have worn smooth and are fringed with fronds of clear ice like ferns or lace or liver lobes. In other places the surface has cracked along straight planes and angles, and fallen askew as wrecked concrete slabs might. The ice on the bottom layer of these ledges is two or three inches of palest blue-green, solid and translucent. On top it is frosted with opaque, compacted snow.

We pass by the point where the creek divides into a series of capillaries running through groves of aspen, cottonwood, fir, and pine. Here the Forest Service used to maintain a rope bridge that swung out over a torrent in spring and linked up with Glacier Trail angling across the knees of Arrow Mountain.

That bridge has since been taken down. Several years ago Arrow twitched its side ever so slightly, and down slid several thousand tons of trees, boulders, currant bushes, yellow clay, and astounded ground squirrels. The piece that tore loose included a section of the Glacier Trail, maybe a hundred yards long. So the Forest Service officially closed that part of the trail, took the rope bridge down, and built a new wooden bridge up over the falls, half a mile farther up the creek.

Today we pass on through the creekside groves where the rope bridge used to be. Even on the cold winter air one

can still smell the acrid cottonwood leaves. As we come out
of the groves and up onto the rocky ledge of trail again, just
where a rabbit highway descends through the snow to the
open water, we find a scrap of dull white fur hanging, waist
high, from a sapling. On the ground, hitched to the tree
bole with a trapper's metal clips, are the front legs and
frozen head of a jackrabbit. A red explosion stains his chest.
Snow has sifted into his eyes and ears, just a fine, riming
coat. The coyotes have not found it yet. It is the sort of
thing one nudges slightly in the snow with a boot toe and
then passes on by without comment.

We climb over the rocks, along ledges, under the wings
of dark, broody evergreens. Then we scramble up a last
slick slope and onto the new bridge, still smelling, even
now in winter, of the alcohol in its preservative.

From the bridge we look up the falls to where the
water rockets down in spring. It is frozen now in knotted,
trollish clumps, tier descending to tier, until it reaches a
sloping plateau. The creek water falls through these tiers of
scalloped blue-green ice chutes until it spouts, dark and
glistening, from an open-mouthed cavern of aquamarine ice.
Then it disappears under a flat plain of ice, encrusted with
snow. Under the bridge it emerges once more from an
umbrous hole. Animal tracks lead out over the ledge to the
open water.

We cross the bridge and slide down the slope on the far
side of the creek, grasping at branches. The creek is
squeezed here by its vertical walls of granite set narrowly
together, thus creating this cataract. Like a constricted artery
in an apoplectic neck, it thunders with the spring runoff.
But in winter the granite walls are thickened with cascades
of ice, hanging like draperies from its sides, the delicate
aquamarine mottled by whatever minerals leach from the
rocks to the water.

We brush off rocks and sit and stare, hands folded, at
the long, crenelated fingers of ice and are content to be
instructed by the day. We try to hear what it is saying about
long, immobile months, locked in suspension. We look up at
the trees on the ledge above us, aimed like arrows at the
sky. Through them descends the snow, like ashes blown
from some great ice-furnace buried in the heart of the
mountains. The snow here is flakes again, not graupel, its

crystals torn into whirligigs by the battering winds aloft. Because of their erratic shapes, they do not fall straight. I pick out one flake and watch it down, and then another and another. Each spins smoothly to some plateau of air resistance, catches, holds a half second, spins, and falls again. Thus the ashy snow staggers down the sky.

It falls, falls, falls, each flake lost among the piled white already littering the ground. The trees, upright and outward thrust, are self-possessed. And the snow, covering them, catching between their needles, possesses not itself, but all things.

Our destined death is like that: to fall from a great height, to distill out of the sky and be buried in time, under all the other moments and occasions that pile up around and over us.

A chinook blew up during the night, so that, by dawn, the temperature was already up to 30°. According to our one radio station, which is seventy-five miles south and fifteen hundred feet lower, the temperature there is below zero. A layer of supercold air is trapped there in the river valley under a blanket of warm air. We are high enough here to be in the warm air stratum. And one doesn't waste such rare opportunities in winter.

I tie up my snow boots, the padded kind that look like medieval leg-wrappings, and hurry out to see this day. By ten o'clock the temperature is above freezing. The wind feels as gentle as a Gulf breeze. The skin itself recognizes hostility or hospitality in the atmosphere here; the unfrozen air is like a continual kiss.

But the sun, even at midday, casts long shadows across the snow, so acute is its winter angle. That the light should be so bright and the shadows so long strikes the eye as incongruous. The midday world takes on a strange, stage-lit look. The sun first reached our cabin at eight-thirty this morning. Its day's passage only makes a narrow arc at the far southern end of the canyon this time of year.

I start out straight north across Ring Lake. My southern-bred instincts still do not trust this unnatural walking on frozen water. I startle at every sudden noise, expecting to fall through the two feet of solid ice, even though I am walking beside the tracks of a pickup truck. Large bubbles the size of oranges are caught in the ice here.

For several weeks now, the voices of the lakes have been hushed. Like all voices, they speak only by the release of compressed air, and most of that has been belched up by now. The current and changes in temperature inevitably bring up more air from the stream flowing beneath the ice, but, walking over the lake, one hears this only as a dull groan. Or a giant heart lurching erratically beneath one's feet. It is like walking over the hide of some mammoth you had supposed was a corpse and suddenly feeling it thud with a last contraction.

Out on the lake is a good place to look for tracks. They show up like imprints on a clean, smooth page. One has to get out early though because the undeflected wind quickly scours the snow clear. I find one print, almost as long as my own hand, with long, extended claws, that I am convinced belongs to a black bear. And another, five inches long, that looks like a mountain lion's. What enticed them out onto the lake?

Around the edges of the lake are rabbit tracks. Practically everywhere one goes there are rabbit tracks. Cottontails and jackrabbits, the plebians of wildlife and the food source for rarer carnivores. They live in the tangles of tree roots, currant bushes, and long grasses that grow along the water. They venture out onto the snow-covered ice only so far as suits their shortcuts. A rabbit's tracks, wherever you find them, never go far though. Even the large jackrabbits, true hares, actually have an ordinary range of only about a thousand feet. Mostly one sees the tracks emerging from the overhang of a rock and lolloping off to a sagebrush thicket. When they're running at full tilt, the sets of two wide-spaced forefeet and two close set hind feet are at least a couple of yards apart. Still, no single rabbit ventures very far unless it's being chased and is cut off from any entrance to its burrow.

The rabbits make regular highways in the snow with their coming and going, packing it down in uneven ruts. One also sees their tracks atop large rocks and boulders. Do they hop up to these high places to scout out their territory, keep watch for their enemies? Or is it merely creaturely curiosity? Sometimes I imagine they have rabbit convocations in the snow and need some dais, some lapine pulpit from which to address the gathering. If you have ever seen rabbits dancing in the moonlight, you would know this is not as far-fetched as it sounds. At any rate, I would like to catch one scrambling atop a boulder, sitting bolt upright, his ears twitching and nose trembling.

On the eastern bank of the lake I find a different kind of sign. Small holes in the snow, smaller than my fist, where damp dirt, broken leaves, and cone debris have been thrown up by frantic digging. The chipmunks have begun breaking into their winter hoard, taking advantage of the warm chinook to dig the few inches through the snow and into the ground to bring out their buried treasure of fir nuts. They're gorging themselves before the next arctic assault begins, laying down a film of fat to live on in their sleep.

Along the brush moraine I see the tiny tracks of mice, the barest indention upon the white expanse that stretches from bush to bush. Their pattern resembles an embroidered seed stitch. The tail, dragging behind, makes a central line from which the outward angled toes point like leaves on a stem. Sometimes I find the tiny tunnels they dig beneath the surface of the snow to shield them from the eyes of eagles and owls.

I start up the east ridge, following first the daisy-pattern tracks of coyote, then the pointed tulip petals of deer tracks. There are almost as many deer tracks as rabbit tracks here. When ambling along or climbing, the deer have a tendency to drag their cloven toes through the snow, leaving lines connecting each hoof print. One can read where they begin their spring-loaded jackrabbit leaps by the sudden disappearance of these languid connections. Coyote tracks are most often found in single sets. They do not travel in groups like the deer. Predators, I suppose, are almost always solitary. Nor do they drag their feet. Their prints are always sharp and clear.

I sit down on a dry rock beside a big fat onion of a juniper. Bushwhacking uphill in a foot of snow makes one warm and winded. It is pleasant to sit in the sun, basking in December. We have such a hunger for the light these short days. It is almost nine in the morning before we have direct sun now and that is all too soon gone, blocked by the west cliff at two in the afternoon. So I soak up these wintry rays like the chipmunks gorge on their hoard of nuts, laying in a supply of stored sun.

From here I can look back down the slope and see my own tracks moving along the game trails. I can mark the places where I stood still, turned, stumbled in the snow. Far down on the lake I can see my boot prints like a line of marching ants. It gives me a queer feeling, having my past marked across a page of time. There I was, only moments ago. That moment has gone—who knows where—but there is the undeniable sign of it, my trail. And here I am looking down, almost, it seems, on myself climbing the slope below.

Our tracks are everywhere up and down this valley. By the beaver dam, by Lily Pond, along Trail Lake, in among the deserted cabins. They crisscross the paths of rabbits, mice, coyote, deer; braid a pattern of the past. I almost expect to look up and meet myself coming along the trail with the same thoughts in my head, the same worry or contentment, the same expression on my face as when the tracks were made.

What other tracks will I make before this winter is over? Along what way will they lead in the end? These are questions that those devoting themselves to dying cannot ask. No light is allowed yet, not even a glimmer at the end of the long dark tunnel of winter. To ask for light now, to demand it, would be like wanting to see, all at once, all the tracks one would ever make. Who knows if you could even bear the sight? Wanting to know how things will turn out, what the end of the story will be. What strange demands we make on life. We want to dig up the seed to see if it has sprouted yet, even before the husk has fallen away and the stored starch has been used up. As though the tracks of the past, leading right up to one's very feet, were not enough for contemplation.

I feel an absolute tenderness for those tracks below. When I made them I was absorbed in sagebrush heavy with snow-bloom, with the fragile tunneling of a mouse, with snow shards blowing into the ice on the lake. It is precious to me, that present that is now my past. So why do I ever want to kill the future, to sit on my sunny rock and watch my tracks going on up the slope ahead of me?

Give me grace, Lord, not to dig up the dying seed. Let me not lust for time not yet mine, the deathly desire that runs so deep through all our race.

Third Sunday in Advent

At church this morning there is a baptism. The small children are called forward first to be instructed and then to witness the rite. The parents and godparents, themselves young, shuffle into place around the font that has been shifted over in front of the altar. There is scarcely room in the small space for the vicar, the godparents, and the baby's family.

The mother, a girl with long honey hair who works at the post office, is the sponsor for the child and answers the questions on behalf of her infant daughter, promising on her part to renounce the works of Satan. The baby smiles in her long batiste baptismal dress. Her two-year-old sister reaches up to paddle her fingers in the font, but a watchful godmother catches her hand and holds it. The baby gives only one small cry when the water runs into an eye. Then she's handed back and handed around. At once she is again amiable, a perfect, blinking dumpling of a baby.

Afterward there is coffee and cookies in the parish hall, decorated now for Christmas. The parents are congratulated, the baby kissed, and her good manners commented upon. How nice, everyone says, to have a baby baptized in this season of the Baby.

Then we drive home again up the canyon. Where we turn off the highway and start to climb up over the rocky road we pass a house in which another daughter lies dying of cancer. She is a college student who came home from school for the last time in October. She is not expected to live till Christmas, two weeks away. I do not know her or her family, but every Sunday the church prays for them.

Her mother, I understand, has no little bitterness over her daughter's dying. She too, no doubt, would like to renounce, defy even, what she sees as the works of Satan, except that somehow they are intertwined with the will of God, and therefore she can neither bless nor curse effectively. And bitterness is the fruit of that frustration.

What a perfect figure of Mary, these two mothers today. The one, young and eager and proud and pondering. The other, with leisure now by her daughter's deathbed to ponder Simeon's aside to Mary in the temple: *And a sword shall pierce your own soul too.* A saying called a blessing by Scripture, but one that later must have torn Mary herself between blessing and cursing. Today's two mothers: Mary at the cradle, Mary at the grave. Rejoicing and bitterness.

Even in Advent the promise and prophecy of Simeon throws a shadow into the future. *A sword shall pierce your own soul too.* Death. Inevitable death, necessary death to us. But unreasoning death, unspeakable pain and reproach to every mother who outlives her child and cannot save it or turn aside the suffering that descends upon it.

Every time I pass that house on the road—a fine big house made of cedar, built I've been told by the parents' own hands—I hold my breath and know only to pray for mercy for it. There lies death. And something worse than death. Life that would die for another but is refused. Dull suffering and bitterness. The mother will not come out of the house but sits by her drugged daughter, hating Satan, hating God. If there is any hope for such a poor, sore heart, it must be in somehow dying.

At such times one feels like calling on Mary, her own heart pierced with the same sword, for mercy for this mother. Mary by the crib, Mary by the cross; bearer of life, powerless at death, comfort this crazed grief that wants no comfort.

Motherhood means death as much as life. Indeed, death came into the world, as Irenaeus says, through the world's first mother. "Eve was disobedient; for she did not obey when as yet she was a virgin. And even as she, having indeed a husband, Adam, but being nevertheless as yet a virgin . . . , having become disobedient, was made the cause of death, both to herself and to the entire human race." After Eve, life no longer came fresh and directly from the hand of the Creator. The first life, as Irenaeus explains it, came from "God's will and Wisdom and from virgin earth. For 'God had not rained,' says the Scripture, before man was made, 'and there was no man to till the earth.' From this earth, then, while it was still virgin God took dust and fashioned the man, the beginning of humanity."

The earth, as the virgin mother of man, was perfectly poised for that purpose. And even now, the dust in us is the truest thing about us. It goes on operating, its molecules as obedient to the structure of their creation as the intervening will of Eve will allow. The earth was our grandmother even before Eve was our mother, a poor dumb grandmother without will or words of her own, one bent solely on being true to her created nature. Perhaps our inheritance from her is all that saved us from the fate of the loftier Lucifer. If we had been made from light instead of dust, who knows how far we might have fallen?

When Jeremiah roared, "O earth, earth, earth, hear the word of the Lord!" he was certain of a better hearing than when he called to the children of Eve, pursuing their own destruction.

Eve only put forth her hand, and with that negligent gesture brought down with her both her own mother and her children. Ever after, life has come the hard way, through the long, dark, contracting passage, pushed out unwilling into the light. It comes through blood and labor and pain. No wonder Jesus insisted on another way of being born, another way of coming to life. Our mother's way is death's way.

Irenaeus, ever one with an eye for symmetry, sees Mary as the mother Eve was meant to be, the key that unlocks the door that leads back to our true state: "so also did Mary, having a man betrothed to her, and being nevertheless a virgin, by yielding obedience, became the cause of salvation, both to herself and the whole human race." All this mirroring so "that morality be absorbed in immortality, and Eve in Mary, that a virgin, become the advocate of a virgin, should undo and destroy virginal disobedience by virginal obedience."

But that was not the end of the story. It was not all accomplished with one angelic *Hail Mary* and a valiant answering Magnificat. There was the birth, bloody as anyone's. There was still her child's mature madness to endure, the madness bent on hurling itself onto the cross. And there was the foot of the cross, the relinquishment of her very motherhood, and then, finally, her child's death. The dead body to take down, to wind, not in swaddling clothes this time, but in a shroud, and to put away in a grave.

Consider the anguish of Mary in Advent. First to bear this child and then to be rebuked by his death. Why is she always shown large-eyed and blue-gowned? Shouldn't she rather be pictured as Medea, in black and wild with grief?

"Let us like Mary bear Christ into the world," the

prayer book said this morning. Well. If we take up such a task, let us remember that we, like Mary, are also promised a sword to pierce our souls.

Sweet baby, baptized this morning. With what innocent abandon we human beings perform these rites upon our children. The white batiste baptismal dress, the grins of the godparents as they pass this daughter of Eve around, the water dripping clear and easy off her head, the celebration dinner afterward. They are baptizing this child, ivory and fresh-fleshed, into death. "Do you not know that all of us who have been baptized into Christ Jesus were baptized into his death?" Your mother, little girl, has given you death for an heirloom, first when she pushed you out into this world and again today when she gave you to God. You've started on your way back to him already, and the only way there is, is as narrow and dark as the way into this world.

The snow is blowing off the lakes like grit in a southwest desert dust storm. We spend the day getting the cabins ready for our Christmas guests. Do the dead make beds for other people?

The Audubon Christmas bird count is today. My visiting sister-in-law and I are assigned to an area that includes a friend's farm along the Wind River. We pack our lunches and take our time about starting out because the wind is still fierce.

When we get to the farm, we crawl into an ancient Land Rover with my friend. She maneuvers the vehicle up onto a sagebrush bench behind the farm buildings. She keeps horses pastured there in winter, and we find them huddled up against a fence corner. Horses, unlike cows, can be left on the range in winter. Their hoofs are made so that they can paw through snow and find fodder under the drifts. These horses have grown shaggy, unkempt coats for the winter. The sun catches obliquely in their long red and gold hairs.

In the groaning Land Rover, we crawl higher up among the limberpine and the rocks. No one is anxious to get out and face the wind. And of course we've seen no sign of a bird. They are all sensibly riding out the gale, hidden behind the branches.

Finally, we pull into a protected ravine and climb out, spreading out in different directions to inventory the trees on a south-facing ridge. Alone and out of the wind, I hear a bird voice, an irritable sort of squeak, and start up the slope to find it. It zigzags, invisibly, from tree to tree. I follow it higher up the slope, all the way to the top of the ridge. It never shows itself. I do not even hear it call any more.

Suddenly, I find myself in snow up to my thighs. Down on the flats the snow was like surf, blown into peaks on the leeward side of brush and rocks, but only thinly covering the ground. Here, held among the trees and boulders, the snow is deep and crusted with ice. I make my way cautiously down the slope again, working my way from one handhold on a branch to another, sliding on my backside in the steep places. So far I haven't scored a single sparrow.

At the bottom of the ridge we regroup and descend the shelf behind the farm. Here there are springs and coverts of willow and alder and wild roses. We have hopes of sighting something in this sheltered area. We stumble through magenta spikes of dried dock and ochre thistles flaking away in seedpods. A pair of deer and two snowshoe hares are all we flush from cover in our descent.

My sister-in-law stops to gather some of the dried weed stalks for Christmas decorations. We pass the corrals at the bottom of the shelf and a flock of barnyard sparrows flies up. But what are barnyard sparrows? They hardly seem worth counting. What we need is a ptarmigan or a sage grouse.

Bird-counting does this to you. Maybe any kind of counting. It's as bad as photography. It narrows one's perception of the world. You begin to lust for rare species. Magpies and sparrows don't matter, don't "count."

We are coming to the river now though, the largest body of open water for miles around. Surely something will show up there. We thrash through brush and over ice-coated stones to get to the water's edge. Something is clattering in the cottonwoods on the far bank. The other side of the river, however, is someone else's territory. Whatever it is will not count on our score. We don't even haul out the binoculars to look.

The sun is dipping ever lower, nearing the rim of the foothills. Still nothing much marked down. We climb through the fence and back up onto the farm lane, heading downstream with the river. Then as we cross a little footbridge over a spring, there, in a juniper tree, a bird announces its presence. We creep quietly beneath it, but there is no real need for stealth. A whole colony of birds has taken over the tree and does not appear inclined to leave it for the evening. One of us gets out the glasses for a closer look while the other fumbles with frozen fingers in the field guide. Crested head. Gray. Yellowish belly. A tidy bird. And six of them the same.

"Cedar waxwing," announces my sister-in-law.

I look skeptical. They are not ordinarily a winter bird here. "Bohemian, maybe?" I suggest.

"No, no. Look. Here. See? The eye markings are different. And there's no yellow on the Bohemian waxwing."

She's right. As a desert-dweller, totally unfamiliar with Wyoming birds, she has made a haul of six cedar waxwings. Maybe because she didn't know she wasn't supposed to see them.

We make our way on down along the river. The waxwings have turned our luck. A dark little dipper, a water ouzel, is diving madly from a rock into the current, jumping out, bobbing up and down, and throwing itself in again to the icy waters of the Wind. Further downstream a Barrow's goldeneye, our only duck of the day, is plowing against the current, making sinuous dunks and dives under the water for his supper. And just in time. The sun is going down, the thermometer says 26°, and the wind is steady at twenty-five miles an hour with stronger gusts. Now that we've accumulated a respectable score, we're ready to give up and go in and drink tea.

Predators in the wild, birds in particular, develop what is called a "searching image." If they come across a number of the same kind of caterpillar, for instance, that image is reinforced in their minds, and the images of other kinds of prey fade. It is as though a template for that particular kind of caterpillar is produced in the brain so that the bird combs its hunting grounds thoroughly for the shape and color that will fit that template. Birds will overlook other sources of forage available to them in the same area, so locked into that singular search are they.

Humans, of course, are similarly inclined at times. We've

been looking for birds today. That has been our searching image. Thus, the deer and the snowshoe hares don't count. Nor the shriveled but still crimson rosehips hanging like bright blood drops against the snow, nor the glowing striations of the badlands on the other side of the river. These would have spoken some mute word to us, but we were bent on birds.

And as usual, our species is capable of compounding the problem. Our searching image is for the rare. Our taste is titillated by the bizarre, even the never-before-seen. What would have pleased us most would have been the sight of a flamingo wading in the Wind or a great auk perched on a boulder up on the bench.

I'm glad the count is over. Now I can go back to looking at chickadees.

Winter Solstice

The sun rises over the ridge at 8:49 this morning and has left our cabin by 2:00 in the afternoon. We have little more than five hours of direct sunlight in the canyon on this the shortest and darkest day of the year. Much of our living is lit by electricity now. Our Christmas visitors have the same reaction to night that our daughter did—they have never noticed how dark night is. Tonight there are only stars and a fingernail of a moon.

For a week the weather has been exceptionally mild. The snow, in fact, began to melt today, earnestly and wetly. No longer does it spray in front of one's boots like fine dust; it balls up in heavy, wet clods. The lakes rumble and cough. Where the current runs through the lake, ice-fishermen have cut out blocks of ice to let their lines down to the water. The blocks have frozen onto the surface and sit like tombstones on top of the lake.

I check for the beaver. I haven't seen him for almost a week, ever since I spotted trappers on Lily Pond. Nothing. A harvest of saplings floats in the stream, their peeled skin pale yellow against the dark open water. But no beaver. No hunched, long-haired back bending industriously over its work.

Some soggy rabbit tracks are all I see of animals today. Those and a mouse who darts behind the bag of cat food on the porch when I turn on the light suddenly. Methodically, I put the cat out.

Four nights ago, on the last Sunday in Advent, the daughter lying in the house by the highway died. She was buried in a grave near the house on the twenty-first, that darkest day of the year. A backhoe was brought in to gouge the grave out of the frozen ground. There was no commerce involved in this death, miraculous as that may seem. The father had built the coffin himself out of native fir. Even the backhoe operator in this small town, where everyone knows the family, donated his machinery and services. So while I was out looking in a desultory way for tracks in the soggy snow, the mother and father and the local vicar were putting this girl to rest in the frozen earth.

It was mercifully warm on the solstice, I remember. They could stand to linger by the grave and take some time over their farewells.

But this afternoon, while we were all out on the lake, holding up our nephews while they learned to skate, it began to snow. The men, who had spent two days building a wind-driven ice-sled, slogged back and forth to the toolshed for yet another wrench to tighten the mast. They had just gotten the contraption to sail several yards when the snow started. It soon was falling so fast and thick that we all had to abandon the lake and the biting teeth of the ice. The younger children were crying with the cold, their small hands red and raw as refugees'.

The snow continued through the night, so that this morning, Christmas Eve, the world has a fresh paint job for the festivities. About six new inches over the old, sunken snow of last week.

After lunch I sneak off to finish framing a painting that is to be a gift for one of my daughters. The varnish is not drying properly in the cold toolshed, so I find a spot in the sun where I hope it will dry enough to wrap it. Then I take off across Trail Lake by myself toward the closed-up summer cabins on the far side.

A Townsend's solitaire calls to me as I angle among the trees there, a single high piping note of great and pure clarity. It looks, if you can ever spot it among the highest conifer branches, like mockingbirds I knew from my childhood, except that mockingbirds are never shy about showing themselves while the solitaire is more often heard than seen. The Townsend's solitaire ranges farther north than any other mountain forest thrush, and when almost all other songbirds desert the Wyoming ranges in winter, it keeps its place here in Torrey canyon as a resident. Though it is reticent and hides itself, it always calls to the passer-by with that single note like the best-tempered bell struck smartly.

I love to hear it call. The sound is like a harpoon aimed right at the heart, and once it lodges there, it plays out a line that tethers the hearer to it. I could live like the Townsend's solitaire today and sit by the lake with the sun glittering on its surface after the snowstorm, sit hidden behind a rock outcropping, and call, once and with passion, to preoccupied passers-by. If I could be anything today, rather than a hostess, mother, wife, I would be a Townsend's solitaire, spying from my hidden perch those who make their way below, anchoring myself to their unregarded beauty.

But to be a solitaire, one must be able to make that single clear note of absolute purity.

At evening, in the early dark, we sit before the fire, all holding candles, like a living birthday cake. Except that, instead of blowing the candles out, we are lighting them one at a time from the white candle on the mantlepiece. We are supposed to say, as each holds his candle to the flame, what Christmas means to us. My sister-in-law remembers Christmas as "the calm in the center of the storm," the storm being her family.

For me it is just the opposite. Whatever calm I may have wrested from the remainder of the year is certain to be destroyed by Christmas. However calm and bright the silent night before Christmas dawns, the day itself is one of the worst ordeals of the year.

As soon as the presents are opened in the morning, a certain fretfulness sets in. Is it from unfulfilled desires, aborted expectations? It has nothing precisely to do with the gifts and whether or not they satisfy. There is always something more, something that remains undefined but essential that we are expecting. Soon we all look like dismal castaways drowning in a sea of ripped wrapping paper and flung ribbon. Tears and tempers are close to the surface. If there is any flaw, any fissure at all in one's character, it will

come out then, at Christmas. The stress of unsatisfied desires
for unremitting joy is so great that the strongest among us
cannot bear the strain. We want God and we get a video
game. In fact, the more we hunger and thirst for him, the
deeper our bewildered distress at the substitutes.

I long for a clean Christmas with no gift but God. With
him we have everything, and I need no distractions from
that bald fact. This Eve, this moment, is clean and clear.
The hearts around this flame open to one another with all
the simplicity that is theirs. If only we could keep within
this pool of yellow light, like children around a birthday
cake, singing in our contentment.

But I do not say these things as I light my candle.
Instead, I say obliquely that I am glad Christmas comes in
winter, out of the very heart of darkness, in the graveyard of
the year. Now, not even the earth, our natural habitat, can
sustain us. We are forced back to the true source of our
lives, that apparently dead seed buried in the heart of the
world, that light that the darkness cannot comprehend.

Christmas Day

It is twelve below zero when we get up. The sun
assaults the snow, and the snow, just as fiercely, hurls back
its rays. Our eyes are caught in this combat zone of light
upon light. We have to squinch up our eyes to keep from
being blinded as we tramp through the drifts. If the
intensity of this cross fire of light on the unbroken expanse
of snowfields is enough to blind us, how much more
dangerous must the unfiltered light of heaven be?

There is noise aplenty in the graveyard of cabins today.
Fires are burning, food cooking, nerves frazzling. There is
the nephews' plastic spaceship to assemble, new clothes to
be tried on for fit, cameras to focus. My corpse is jangled up
and down on a string. I cling to the broccoli I'm cutting up
in the kitchen as a drowning man clings to a mast. There is
a quarrel in the other room over a telephone number.

Only the dead withstand the rumpus of Christmas
morning. Those who have a stake, any stake, in surviving
are overcome by it.

We all go cross-country skiing on Togwotee Pass, named
for the last independent Sheep-Eater chieftain who left the

Yellowstone area to join the Shoshonis at the end of the last century. After that, the Sheep-Eaters, like the dinosaurs, disappeared.

On the way up the pass we discuss the relative visual merits of the mountains in winter versus the mountains in summer. Those who prefer winter argue for the way the snow simplifies the lines of the landscape. Summer, they say, provides too much intricacy of detail and disconcerts the senses. They are willing to accept the austerity of winter, in fact, find its reduced stimuli an avenue to serenity. The summer people argue for movement and color and variety. The only conclusion we reach is that a preference for winter coincides with one for black-and-white photography, while those who like summer also prefer color film. A predictable enough combination.

At dusk the light on the huge snow hummocks on the ski trail turns palest amethyst. No chemical color emulsion could catch its tender, edible quality.

We wake up to a whopper of a snowstorm, unpredicted, as all the worst ones are. In the earliest morning light we watch our elder daughter nose her car out the gate and over the wooden bridge, heading back to Colorado. The storm has already closed the Denver airport.

While she was with us (is she going already?) she has spent only one short evening talking about the person she is determined to love. I recognize the timbre of determination in her voice. It makes me afraid for her. She is determined to love or die. Does she realize yet there's no difference?

She'll go as far as Lander, she says, and check with the highway department to see if she can get through the rest of the way. To her, the storm is only something to match her determination against.

Why am I always having to send my daughters out like this, across the Red Desert, into the teeth of storms? No, not send. Watch them go. I may as well not even be there for all the protection I provide against the outrageous fortune of this world. She makes it up the hill on the other side of the bridge. The red car slows down for the cattleguard and then disappears through the curtain of falling snow.

It snows all day long and never gets above 12°. Everyone mills about the cabin, hoping the others will go for a walk and leave a space for peace behind. When it reaches what I know will be the warmest part of the day, I go out into the dark afternoon. My reward comes down by the creek. The beaver is back! Down in his accustomed spot, stripping sticks. The air is so emptied by the cold that I can hear his teeth grinding away at the bark in staccato rhythm.

I wind along Lily Pond up to Trail Lake and walk out on its flat surface covered with nearly a foot of new snow. Snowmobilers from the campgrounds on the far side of the lake have cleared away circles of snow and cut holes in the ice for fishing. They have set up tripods to hold the lines over the holes—which freeze over again at once. A muffled figure pulling two children on a sled behind a snowmobile passes me and waves through the gloom.

Today is one minute longer than yesterday, although with no sun all day long, it hardly matters. The solstice on the twenty-first was actually only the central point in a nine-day stretch of shortest days of the year. It is on Christmas Day that the light, imperceptibly, begins to increase. By the end of January the day will be fifty-three blessed minutes longer.

Twenty below zero this morning.

I manage to get a call through to our daughter. She made it after all, through a storm that was far worse in Colorado than here in Wyoming.

More of our holiday guests depart, on their way back to the sunny desert. Still below zero here.

The year's last day. A bighorn ram crosses the road right in front of me this morning, his horns spiraling outward in logarithmic curls, like a chambered nautilus. He joins the rest of his herd and nudges one of his neighbors roughly on the chest with his horns, a characteristic way of reminding the others of his dominance. Bighorn sheep aren't subtle.

Considering the condition of this riverbed-road, an amazing number of people come to look at the sheep. During hunting season the bighorns are hard to find, but come winter, they turn, if not friendly, at least cautionless. The cars roll by, big low-slung sedans from Nebraska, vans from Colorado. The sheep ruminate, their golden slit eyes blinking like all wary victims the world over. They have other predators to worry about now, primarily coyotes and the cold.

In the afternoon I take the friend's dogs we have been keeping during the holidays and go for a walk farther up the canyon. For over a week the temperature has stayed well below freezing, but this afternoon, suddenly, there are a few hours of melt. The cold loosens and lets water trickle through its grip. It drips from the cabin eaves.

At first I follow the meanderings of the creek, watching the dogs double back and forth up the hill and down again. Like sprung spirits they dash, nose in the snow, after every wild scent. We come up on a rise overlooking the creek and spot a herd of at least a hundred bighorns grazing in the irrigated meadow below. Descending into the willow flats along the creek again, I pick out a new set of tracks—a good deal larger than those of the sheep. Either elk or moose. Coming face to face suddenly with a moose among the willows where they spend their winter days isn't wise. With the dogs thrashing through the underbrush it's unlikely I'll stumble on one; nevertheless I leave the willows and head up the hill again.

Here are tracks I can plainly identify as elk. Quite fresh, they head straight up the slope toward the heavy tree cover. I can tell they have been made today, possibly even this afternoon, because the spray of snow kicked up on top of the frozen crust is still powder and has not yet begun to dissolve in the warm air and direct sun.

Following the contour of the slope, the dogs and I enter the trees too. The great shaggy spruce are like trees from a troll fantasy. Under a Douglas fir I find squirrel debris, the remains of its midwinter meal. The snow on the trail here has been packed by many cloven hooves. It's a regular elk highway down to the water from the higher forest.

The dogs and I slide down the creek bank through the trees. Down in this narrow floodplain the stream staggers brokenly through heaved roots and rocks and huge windfall tree trunks. The skeleton of a broken stalk of cow parsley sticks above a snowdrift. I touch the pale spoked head, and the dark flat seeds fall and sink into the snow. Little dry catkins of water birch brush against my shoulder and shower the ground. A gooseberry bramble, its thorns thick as fur, is still studded with dark purple fruit. I pull one and it crumbles to freeze-dried powder between my fingers. I rub the hard little kernels free and let them fall into the snow too. On this year's last day I sow my spring crop with these frozen seeds.

I clamber up the incline again and start back through the trees along the elk highway. The dogs raise a rabbit and give that peculiar frantic yelp of one animal impelled to chase another.

The sun is behind us as we come out into the open. Down along the creek the willow flats are rosy in the sunset, so near the color of flame one could almost imagine them warm. But halfway home we cross a ravine filled with frozen runoff from a spring. The color of the ice, heaved and molten where it leaks from the earth, is coldly green like a coke-bottle bottom.

Crossing this frozen canyon floor, the dying sun at my back, I think, for some reason, of my belongings still stored in a concrete bunker in Cheyenne. Here where my furniture is fir trees and willow flats, granite boulders and fossil cliffs, those far-off belongings seem like the lost cargo of a sunken ship. Are mice nibbling, like sea-floor fishes, at the ends of my past? Are they making nests in it? Well, mice have a living to make too. Will I ever have my books again, straight and ordered on a shelf somewhere? And my dishes; and the big bulky mixer I bought at the Goodwill; my summer clothes; my file cabinet full of old work? It would be all too easy never to see it again. To cut it all loose, like a triaged lifeboat. A gesture as simple as brushing the frozen seeds into the snow.

January

January 1

This day doesn't feel like anything new. I'm not satisfied with it as the beginning of anything. To mark the new year at the first of January doesn't make sense. It doesn't correspond to any particular event in the cosmic clock. It's a symbol without a referent.

The whole idea of marking time came to us from the cosmos itself, from the regular and predictable revolutions of heavenly spheres. Egyptians, Babylonians, Algonquins, Aztecs—all used their observations of predictable changes in the astronomy hanging over their heads to tell where they were in relation to the rest of the universe. Even Copernicus didn't alter that. He may have shifted the center of the clock, but time was still a matter of knowing one's place. Over the centuries, the Western mind became so abstracted, however, that it took Einstein to wrench us back to understanding that time is only a function of place. This was a self-evident fact to any Pacific coastal aborigine who waited for the full fish-moon to wash the silver grunion up on the beaches.

Phillip Morrison, a theoretical physicist, has made a comparison between the new quartz crystal watches, which operate by the oscillations of a rotating vector, and the cathedral clock at Wells, crafted during Chaucer's time. This clock has a sunburst as its principal hand, which travels around the dial once in twenty-four hours. It also has another dial within the larger one that marks the phases of the moon. The clock is inscribed (in Latin) thus: *This circular dial presents the universe in microcosm.*

It was the clock as a model of the moving cosmos that was important in Chaucer's day, not its practical schedule-keeping function. The point of Morrison's comparison is that arbitrary, abstracted computation, such as that provided by digital clocks, cannot furnish the human mind with the analogues it needs for refulgent comprehension. The attenuated picture of the cosmos we get from a digital clock "is too narrow, it is too thin, and we will not be fully nourished on such a diet, however precise and however numerous the bits which it can handle." The day, the month, the year, are all matters of rotation, and the round-faced clock with its revolving hands is a much better image of that fact than the numbers that blip electronically on a watch face with no visual connection to how much of the hour has passed and how much is to come. It is an almost totally abstracted model, with no past and no future visible, no relationship to anything else, least of all to the reality it is supposed to represent. You cannot "see" a quarter of an hour there, only the present minute that itself vanishes into oblivion with the next pulse. And perhaps our artifacts, watches among them, are analogues for more than the measurement of time. Perhaps the vanishing numeral is also a figure of our own feared futility.

This is why January 1 is so pointless to me. It represents nothing of the reality of the universe. It is not the beginning of spring or any other season. It is not tied to the phases of the moon or the sun. The solstice, the darkest part of the year, is already too far past. This date is only a number; it echoes no further reality for us. It is not deep enough to hold even a seed.

As one might expect, it became the first of the year by political fiat. Julius Caesar chose the date in 46 B.C. (although of course he couldn't have known that it *was* 46 B.C.). Its one link to a larger reality is in the month's being named for Janus, the double-faced god who looks both forward and backward, guardian of portals and patron of beginnings and endings, no doubt intended by Caesar to be a symbol of that caesura between the past and the future.

The ancient world operated successfully in fact with any number of variant calendars. Besides the civil Julian calendar, the Jews had their own way of measuring the year in lunar phases, using a calendar that began with the last new moon in September. The Essenes, however, that ascetic Jewish sect, found the lunar calendar too common for their purposes and called it "an abomination of the Gentiles." They insisted instead on a solar calendar, which they claimed they had inherited from an ancient Zadokite tradition based on the laws of "the Great Light in heaven."

At first the Christian church did not much concern itself with when to begin the year, though it did warn against participating in the Roman Saturnalia that marked the end of the old year. In fact, with a spirit of charity unknown in our own day, the church went so far as to institute special fasts and masses of expiation for the souls of their pagan neighbors who had celebrated too much. We still have the Saturnalia to contend with today. But just as our quartz crystal watches with digital displays are inadequate models for the cosmos, our New Year's Eve parties with their paper hats and whistles and champagne at a flat rate, are pale imitations of Rome's massive, purgative, midwinter debauchery. Moderns don't make very good pagans. Our hearts are not in it. We're better at quiet desperation.

Probably at an early stage, however, the church began marking its time by its principal celebrations, Easter and Pentecost, which, being dependent on events in the Jewish lunar calendar, were, like Passover, movable feasts.

It wasn't until the sixth century (again, no one knew that it *was* the sixth century till then) that Dionysius Exiguus, calculating from the Feast of the Annunciation, reckoned backward to A.D. 1, when the world had begun anew on March 25. After that, the Christian world celebrated the New Year as the anniversary of the Annunciation when the Creator entered his own creation.

Later, after Christianity had spread to northern Europe, a variety of New Year traditions flourished, all still related to the liturgical year. Germany, for instance, celebrated Christmas and the New Year together. France and the Low Countries observed Easter as the time of the beginning. But England continued to hold to the Annunciation, March 25, until the rather late date of 1752, almost two centuries after the reform of the calendar by Pope Gregory XIII.

Gregory, trained as a canonical lawyer, found the imprecision of the Julian calendar irritating. By 1582 it had already accumulated ten extra days because of failing to account for the extra six hours it took the planet to circumnavigate the sun every year. With this Gregorian reform of the Julian calendar, January 1 was reestablished as the official New Year's Day, at least in the Western world. And now we are stuck with this disjunctive and arbitrary civil date that mirrors nothing of consequence either in the liturgical or the cosmic cycle we call a year.

Certainly the land I live on takes no particular notice of this first day of January. The solstice, the farthest point on the planet's pendulum as this hemisphere swings away from the sun, occurred over a week ago. The light has been increasing ever since. We've put up a fresh calendar, but it is illustrated, incongruously, with an unfolding fiddlehead fern. One feels slightly off balance trying to fit into this schema that doesn't fit anything in the observable universe.

Late in the afternoon we spot, just across the creek, a moose cow and her calf meandering through the campground where the ice-fishermen stay. Moose are absurdly shaped animals. They would look like donkeys except for the hump across their shoulders, a pendulous snout, and disproportionately long legs. But as the cow and her calf start to amble off, back up the canyon toward the willow flats, they break into an unexpectedly elegant lope. It is a curious, almost dancing trot. Like giraffes, they appear to float in supple undulations despite their awkward assembly.

What are this mother moose and her baby a sign of? How does one take them into account when internally modeling the cosmos and time? I don't know. But I call this Moose Day, even New Moose Day, in honor of the calf.

In the middle of the afternoon I looked down from the slope above Ring Lake where I had stopped to rest against a rock and saw an unfamiliar vehicle pull up beside our cabin half a mile away. Reluctantly I started slogging back through the drifted snowfields. It must be late holiday visitors or someone lost.

Our younger daughter and her college roommate are still here for the rest of their winter vacation. I found them inside, pouring coffee and serving muffins to the local vet and his wife. One of the dogs we've been keeping for our friend had been caught in a trap farther up the canyon. The girls had taken them for a walk up to the sheep meadow. Neither they nor the man in a pickup they had flagged down had been able to get the trap off the dog's leg. By the time the vet and his wife had arrived to rescue her, she had cut up her mouth a good bit, biting and pulling at the heavy metal jaws and chain.

A mountain lion, the vet says. They must have been after a mountain lion at least to use a trap that big. It was up on a rocky hillside where anyone—dog, sheep, human— might have stepped in it, not hidden down in the shrubby creekside brush where coyote traps are usually set. He's treated three dogs caught in traps in the past few weeks. It couldn't have been meant for a beaver either, he says. No one's buying beaver now. The market's down. The only people who'll pay to have them trapped are hay farmers who don't want their irrigation systems clogged.

The girls are still edgy after their three-hour ordeal, most of it spent sitting on the hill beside the frantic animal. They're angry and want to write a letter to the editor of the local paper. They don't realize how people live here. They are students and read books about criminal justice, bioethics, war, and peace. In such an atmosphere the illusion persists that life consists of a series of problems, each with a discoverable solution.

The vet, a man of curling gray hair who has moved here from San Francisco and affects a bandana around his neck, is more direct. Spring every trap you come on, he says. Better yet, carry them home. That discourages trappers.

I ask him if it isn't against the law to spring traps.

He shrugs. Who'll know? Of course, he adds, you might get some people mad at you.

The vet and his wife finish their coffee, leave some antibiotics for the dog, and drive away, back toward town. The girls are still intermittently tearful. The dog licks her forepaw and goes to sleep, exhausted. I tell them not to worry; everything will be all right. I don't remind them that people like to kill other animals, preferably large ones, and there's nothing we can do about it. I don't say that they do this for fun and make laws to protect this pleasure. I don't point out how much in love with death our species is. They're already crying.

About sundown a crowd of snowmobilers pull into the campground across the creek, tearing the air with their shouts and two-cycle engines. If they fell through the ice, there would be a moment, right before I caught myself, when I would be glad.

This morning there is a small herd of bighorn sheep on the peninsula across the stream from the cabin. They paw through the snow, looking for forage. Rabbitbrush protrudes through the snow there, stripped of its small lance-shaped leaves. The animals are now down to eating that. Rabbits, deer, sheep—whatever has delicate enough lips to tug the leaves from the stems and leave the plant denuded.

What to eat gets to be a problem this time of year. Snow covers the tough, nourishing dried grass of the meadows. Only the shrubby plants stick above it. The animals put off eating sagebrush as long as they can.

A good many species deal with winter food shortages by migrating, which is, in fact, what the sheep have done. They have come down from their home on the high peaks to these lower meadows where the snow is not as deep. This is the elk's pattern too. Most of the birds in this canyon move off to warmer regions in the winter, sometimes as far as the Southern Hemisphere. The ones that stay are those whose food supply remains: the chickadees and Clark's nutcrackers that cling to the fir cones, sometimes hanging upside down to pull the kernels out; the solitaires that scrabble around for insect larvae at the foot of large evergreens; the hawks and owls and eagles, birds of prey whose living is perhaps even easier to make in winter when the mice and rabbits show up distinctly against the white background. And always the scavenger magpies.

Some mammals, mostly small rodents, hibernate in order to save themselves from starvation. Bears, though depicted in popular lore as hibernators that wake hungry and ferocious in spring, are not considered true hibernators by zoologists. Their body temperatures do not drop far enough during their long winter's sleep. Nor are cold-blooded animals—frogs, turtles, snakes—technically hibernators, since they lack the capacity to reverse the process and rouse themselves. They are at the mercy of external heat sources to thaw them out. All true hibernators are self-starters. They can wake themselves from their own torpor and periodically do during the winter. I often see signs of chipmunks and squirrels who have waked themselves and gone out to grab a bite from their buried hoard of nuts at the foot of a tree.

A few birds, being warm-blooded, are also hibernators. Whippoorwills and nighthawks, who depend on a diet of insects, sometimes sleep steadily through the long night of winter.

Around here, the primary hibernators are the rodents— mice, picketpins, chipmunks, gophers, and ground squirrels. Like all mammals, they function best when their body heat is around 98° F, at which temperature the rapid chemical reactions within the cells that are characteristic of mammalian metabolism can best take place. Hibernation is a process that simply damps down these internal fires. When a marmot, one of the high, rock-dwelling mammals here, hibernates, its brain temperature drops to 68°. Further north, an arctic ground squirrel's plummets to 42°. The heart rate takes a corresponding dive, dropping to only a few beats per minute. The electrical activity of the brain all but shuts down completely. The animal's blood supply to outer regions of its body is constricted, and its primary circulation is concentrated in the more vulnerable heart and brain. Cold paws, warm heart.

The human heart, however, will fail when cooled to only 75° F, a temperature that, externally, seems ideal to us. Humans can take refuge neither in dormancy, like the cold-blooded animals, nor in hibernations, like certain of our warm-blooded kin. What is hibernation for them is hypothermia for us. The range of conditions within which we can sustain life is much narrower than theirs. Perhaps because we need something deeper than sleep. We need death. Not just a nap to tide us over a lean season, but disintegration. Can anything less cure us of our love of death except dying?

I think we try to substitute hibernation for death, however. We will cut back, we think, especially after the gluttonous holidays, preferring to diet rather than die. We'll slow down, maybe make a retreat, get our priorities straight. Reform, make resolutions. Asceticism always seems particularly appealing after the satiation of fruit cake and pralines.

We have intentions toward austerity. We'll simplify our lives, shovel out the trivia. Clean house. Meditate more. Learn to lower our heart rate with biofeedback.

But this is not death. Not the necessary death that must go on, continually, seasonally, repeating itself. "Self will come to life even in the slaying of the self," George Macdonald insisted. No wonder we are so eager to accept the reduced circumstances after Christmas and the New Year. We sense the need for a scouring of the self, knowing we cannot go on with this tattered scarecrow much longer, any longer, but we hope to get by with a mere cutback, a hibernation, a mimicry of death. We hope we can avoid having to face the real thing.

Hibernators have the power of self-initiated waking.
That's the way we want our deaths—entirely at our disposal.
We'd like to make a plan: On such and such a day I shall
die. Lie down and drift peacefully into it. And then, after a
seemly time sleeping, on another such day, I'll wake up,
reconstituted, like a butterfly within its chrysalis.

Christians are big on butterflies. What they don't realize
is that the caterpillar undergoes complete dissolution within
those chitin walls, turns to mush, undifferentiated slime,
before its cells are rearranged into the new, flying creature
it becomes.

The purpose of hibernation is entirely different from the
purpose of death. Hibernation is a hedge against death. It is
conservative. It saves the old life. No doubt the creatures
who hibernate, hoarding their starches in their complex fat
cells, are worth saving as they are.

But we are not, you and I. Our current mode of
existence is imperfect, incomplete. You must feel it too, that
straining against sloth, against the reptilian brainstem, that
backward fall into inadequacy. I do not put this to you as a
matter of morality. It is not a matter of being good; it is a
matter of being perfect. Morality is at best only a stopgap; a
snow fence; a sea wall. If we were perfectly fulfilling our
destiny, morality would have no meaning, would be beside
the point. For a helium atom, there is no such thing as
morality.

But there are holes in us, great moth-eaten holes, and
through them we are leaking away into oblivion. We are all
less than we are capable of imagining—less wise, less true,
less simple, less beautiful. And each of these imperfections
is a fissure through which seeps our strength and our hope.
Don't try stopping those cracks with your moral practices—
not your chastity, your temperance, your pacifism, your
generosity. No matter how chaste, temperate, gentle, or
generous you are, it will never be enough. Not enough to
stop the holes where chaos sucks at your very substance. It's
not just money you can't take with you to the grave; you
can't take your virtues either. If all you have in mind is
hibernation, then by all means tuck away the odd good deed
to dig up again for a lean winter day. But hibernation does
not end in metamorphosis. The same creature will crawl out
of its hole at the end of the winter, only weaker and

hungry. Butterflies do not eat at all inside the chrysalis. They simply turn to jelly. To be re-created demands at least that much.

The last of our guests left yesterday. We drove the college girls to the bus station ninety miles away and put them on the bus back to their other lives. Then we came back to our own. Back to where we left off three weeks ago. The holy days have not changed our need to die.

The midwinter festival is a bonfire in the year's dark night. It probably had more power when the night was actually darker. Now we have artificial lights and can fly off to Florida. Both the darkness and the light, therefore, mean less to us.

Be that as it may, outside now the sheep and the deer are pawing through the snow for something to eat. And the weeks that lay ahead for us must also mean dearth and death.

For the past several days we have been living in a false spring. It is expected about this time in January. Following hard on the heels of the year's coldest weather will come a sudden thaw lasting perhaps a week. Even at night the thermometer has barely gone below the freezing mark. I remember the false springs of Texas and the Midwest. Shirt-sleeve weather when we worried that the fruit trees and flowering shrubs would go wild and burst their buds, only to freeze again the following week. But while it lasted, everyone enjoyed the sun, the warmth, the unwonted ease.

January's false spring in Wyoming is not like that, but then neither is its true spring. Here the rising temperatures mean one thing—rising winds. As the air thaws out, it begins to move. It drives from the west, increasing its speed and fury as it funnels through the mountain canyons. Its ferocity is like an animal that has been confined, immobilized in ice, and is now free to ravage the land at will.

Day before yesterday it snowed steadily all day long while the temperature hovered at freezing. But for all the myriad flakes that went flying past the windows, none of them collected on the ground. It is what we call a horizontal snow. Like time, no one seems to know where it goes. Does it just evaporate in the wind? Does it make it to the Midwest where it finally settles in a flurry? Does it simply blow back and forth between the walls of the canyon until it wears itself down to an invisible nub?

Ragged clouds tear across the sky, the dark gray and gun-metal clouds that hold water in its opaque liquid form. At evening they bleed into one another in shades of mauve and coral like watercolor clouds.

The angle of the sun gives it away, however, this false spring. Spring's light is direct and penetrating, while the January sun retains that oblique slant peculiar to stage lighting. The shadows, even at noon, are long across the land.

We lie in bed at night and listen to the wind buffet us. It is like being on a ship, a small one, in the middle of a gale. Gravel and grit from our roof rattle down the stove pipe. Drafts blow in even around the storm windows. In the morning we discover that the wheelbarrow we left over-turned across the dwindling woodpile has been blown to the barbed-wire fence behind the cabin.

After several days of thaw, big puddles collect on top of the frozen lakes. Snowmobilers will have a slushy time of it this weekend. The only ones who really benefit from the false spring are the herbivores—the deer, sheep, and rabbits whose forage emerges from the sinking snow.

It is more uncomfortable to be out in 35° weather with a wind like this than it is to walk around in still, zero air. And it takes even more wood to heat the cabin when the wind sucks at it so ravenously.

For Wyoming, the false spring is no relief from winter. No one suffers any delusion of warm and easy days ahead. We know what we're up against. The worst may be yet to come. We huddle against the wind, sit tight, wait for the blessed stillness to descend again with the cold.

Epiphany Sunday

Mary Back, in her chalk-talk children's sermon this morning, was trying to outline the white-robed angels in her picture with black charcoal so that they would show up better. "Well," she said and paused for a long moment (she finds it hard to draw and talk at the same time), "this is all light, and when something is all light, you can't see it."

I know what she means. When I walk across a perfectly

smooth, untouched snowfield, the surface reflects so much sunlight that, looking down, one cannot judge distance at all. No distinctions are possible. The world before your eyes becomes Nirvana Land, pure and simple. No shapes emerge unless there is a sharp edge of a drift to catch a shadow. We cannot see, not with our present equipment, without shadows. There would be no distinctions, no separate shapes without them. All of life would be a vast undifferentiated snowfield, blinding in its intense, reflected light.

As the hymn says, the immortal, invisible God is hid from our eyes by light inaccessible. Only the shadows make accessible what little we know about life.

For those who have found my subject too grim, I offer this defense: I am only drawing with a black stick of charcoal an outline to make certain figures clear.

On this Epiphany Sunday we also sing about myrrh, one of the gifts the three kings brought to the infant Messiah. It symbolizes, so the song says, the death to come, hanging over the cradle. A shadow falling around the radiance of the angel chorus.

Mary, the Scripture for the day says, kept all these things and pondered them in her heart. The heart, you will remember, that was to be pierced by a sword. Did she tuck away this treasure of the magi with a doubtful smile, keeping it as an heirloom to give her son, along with the strange story, when he grew up and had a home of his own one day? Was this Christmas-present myrrh one of the spices she took to the tomb to anoint her son's body?

Primitive tribes sometimes startle Western missionaries at Christmas by enacting, not the manger scene, but the Crucifixion. In their remarkable capacity for nonlinear thinking, they perceive the entire rondure of the story simultaneously, the end inherent in the beginning. They don't miss the point of the myrrh.

How are we weak-kneed Westerners, who have not the courage to recognize the death impending in the birth, who want to celebrate Christmas and Epiphany as one long season of unrelieved if artificial light, who delete the last verse of Simeon's song and ignore Herod's slaughter of the innocents—how are we ever to face the shadows that aborigines accept so easily? We have no forty-percent mortality rate. Disease does not bring premature darkness to our eyes. Our crops do not fail. We have never seen anyone starve except in pictures. Our lack of experience puts us at a disadvantage when finally we must face certain stark realities. We are undone by death because of its unfamiliarity. We do not sleep in our coffins like the Capuchins. And we try to forget the myrrh, sitting there among the gifts like a time bomb. The myrrh is a reproach, a reminder of why the child is there at all, a hostage to death.

How can we bear it? How can we possibly bear it, the dramatic irony of the wise men presenting the gift of death to the newborn God? Why, when we pour from the church, the taste of his blood still in our mouths, why do we love the sound of the bell ringing, long and loud, announcing all over the little town, to the drugstore on the corner, the gas station doing a desultory Sabbath business, the stale odors of the Rustic Pine bar, the steamy interior of the Grub and Tub Washateria, why do our own hearts fly up and out also, like pigeons disturbed from the belfry by sudden joy, flapping and wild with victory?

The Lord is gracious, even to us. I cling to the promise of today's Old Testament lesson; I intend to remind the Lord of it often. *A bruised reed he will not break, nor a dimly burning wick he shall not quench.* Bruised and smoldering, we need to give thanks while we can. We need to grab the moment with the bell rope and spend it wildly. Quickly.

Do not worry that joy is not now our perpetual state. Be greedy. Snatch it and stuff it away before the dark descends again. It is no less real for being transitory. Feed on it in your heart through the long night when no bell rings. Give thanks while you still have the strength.

The wind, the wind, the unremitting wind. For a week it has assaulted us without ceasing. Waking and sleeping, indoors and out, its noise is a continual roar, bellow, blast, shriek. From down below on the canyon floor, we hear it high on the tops of the ridges, rumbling like a rocketing freight train. Making the stovepipe shudder, whipping the reaching limbs of the trees, sailing snow in enormous clouds across the lake. In some places people wait for such a gale to blow itself out. But not in Wyoming. This is the origin and heartland of winds. They are manufactured here.

A power company set up an experimental wind turbine just outside Medicine Bow. Its propellers were immediately wrecked and mangled by the wind it was supposed to harness.

The porch roof of one of the cabins higher up blew off two nights ago. It sags several feet on one corner now, the support post dangling like a broken bone. Roofing paper litters the snow all around.

The great roaring wind of Pentecost must have been engendered in Wyoming. Fierce and implacable, blowing at eighty miles an hour, these winds bend everything before them—beast, plant, man. The stones themselves wear away under their breath. This wind blows where it wills. Ruthless in its own hidden purposes, oblivious to the entreaties of the lowly, earth-gripping creatures.

Jesus made a play on words with wind and spirit, trying to teach us its wildness. The wind blows where it wills. But, as with all things spiritual, we have tried to tame it. If anyone really wants a taste of the Spirit, let him come to Wyoming, climb Gannet Peak, and there, struggling to stand upright in the blast of suffocating snow that can suck the breath right out of his lungs, there let him dare to mutter his platitudes about the Spirit. When the Lord answered Job, it was out of the whirlwind, a typhoon, a hurricane. And after his baptism in the Jordan, the Spirit *drove* Christ into the wilderness, drove him the way the wind drives the leaves, the waves, the snow before it.

Those who try to tame this wind had better beware. Try to harness its power and you may end up like the Medicine Bow wind turbine. Better to let it drive you, head over heels, into the wilderness.

There was a strange, soothing sound in the air when I went out to bring in wood for the fire this morning; it took a long moment before I recognized it. The sound of running water. The creek has thawed its thick shell of ice clean through, and the sound of living water, moving and free, was abroad. It was a lovely sound and entered my ears as gently as health returning to an invalid. We know, of course, it will not last. The stream will freeze again and bury the sound of running water under the ice once more. But life sends its tokens ahead of it, as surely as death does. The sound is as certain a sign as the bones I picked up in the summer, although I cannot put it in my pocket. It is merely the nature of life in the kingdom of this world to be fragile and fleeting while death is solid and lasting.

I write about emptiness after the fact, as must be. When one is empty, nothing floats up from the depths of memory to be caught with the hook of consciousness and spread out on paper. One must sit and wait and *be* empty.

The evacuation of our guests from our lives left us for a time in a vacuum. The snow has rotted from the slopes and along with it the scenery. The romance of the storms has receded, and all we are left with is the drudgery of the world's dying now.

I recall an account of a country funeral in nineteenth-century America.

> Everyone as he entered, took off his hat with his left hand, smoothed down his hair with his right, walked up to the coffin, gazed down upon the corpse, made a crooked face, passed up to the table, took a glass of his favorite liquor, went forth upon the plat before the house, and talked politics, or the new road, or compared crops, or swapped heifers or horses, until it was time to lift.

That's where we are now. We've tipped our hat, pulled our long face, slugged down our favorite liquor, and are now outside upon the plat, discussing mundane matters. Death is only dull now. No longer dangerous even. The year has died and simply lies there, waiting for the coffin to be lifted into the ground.

Empty, we grow smaller. Deflated like a used-up balloon. A letter comes from a friend, announcing a long-expected divorce. Well, what does one say? "I'm sorry"? So what. A marriage has died. This is an affront to the universe. Wedding, in all its diminutive and dilated forms, is what holds the world together. We are to sacrifice our lives for it, "even as Christ also loved the church, and gave himself for it." We hold out against chaos by our fidelity.

But vacuum happens. The heart suddenly goes out of us. We can no longer hold the fort. We crumble and collapse, and the rats run over our ruins. That's life, we say; meaning, of course, that's death.

Well, what can I say? Nothing tonight. I take up the

letter again, but my head aches and my fingers are empty of words. Thus is life fragile. A few milliliters too much fluid in the sinuses and we are useless to our friends, have no sandbags to throw up against invading chaos, certainly no comfort. Ask for me tomorrow and you'll find me a grave man, as the dying Mercutio said to his friend Romeo.

Teilhard de Chardin, the Jesuit paleo-theologian, wrote about "passive diminishment," a relinquishment of our power to stave off affliction and loss. Paul came to treasure his own weakness because it provided a vacuum into which the Spirit was then sucked to do its will. And weakness is preferable to pride.

There is a sense in which death is definition, definition of the self. By excising all the not-me, including all the attempts to be what I can never be and was never intended to be, I can finally pare myself down to the quite small thing I was made for. Self-knowledge is largely a negative activity, like whittling. One defines oneself by knowing what one lacks. Things like words, wisdom, comfort, answers.

And one must be passive before the diminishment, this steady erosion of illusions. Try to grab back any power whatever and it's all to do over again. One must cooperate with one's own deflation, be an instrument of one's own death, in order to gain any definition at all. Take the stick of black charcoal and draw the outline closer and closer in, shaving off layers of extraneous, accreted self. Perhaps in the end one will be only the size of a peg, or a needle, or a seed.

I go walking this afternoon in sunlight that is as weak as an invalid's wan smile. Some snow is still snagged between the clumps of sagebrush, but even there it is rotting. The tracks our Christmas guests made are dissolving as the snow melts. I had been keeping them as souvenirs, carefully stepping over them when I go out walking, trying to save the tokens of that time. But the background on which they were made is no longer fresh and white; it looks like a dirty, discarded page, an outdated memo.

The weather, having spent its force on the Christmas storms, is now empty itself of any romantic winter residue. There are still places where the snow is drifted up to my knees, but now it is only a nuisance, an obstruction to walking. Dirt and dead leaves clog it. One thinks of the snow only in practical terms now, of how it is melting from underneath, against the earth that soaks up the moisture for spring. Even watching the footprints disappear is like clearing away the Christmas decorations and getting back to normal.

The lake snorts as I tramp across it. Otherwise the silence is like a huge, trembling note in the stillness after the winds. The thermometer only just makes it up to the freezing mark by midafternoon, but the absolute calm, even though the sun is weak, makes the air seem benign. The surface of the lake is pocked with puddles that have alternately melted and refrozen for a week now. Along the banks are high, hollow drifts we cross gingerly, expecting to crash through with the next step. And we do.

I sit on a rock that juts out of the ice and sun myself like a winter lizard. The dead gray skeletons of thinleaf alders arch out over the frozen lake. If their branching convolutions were turned to sound, they would be a fugue. It is the gift—and the limitation—of the human brain to only understand one thing in terms of another thing. Brother Lawrence, the seventeenth-century Carmelite monk, declared that it was the sight of a tree in winter, stripped of its leaves, that first kindled in him the love of God.

I sit on the rock as long as I can, but eventually the weak sun gets even weaker, and I have to move on to keep from freezing. Having walked out over the lake, I make my way back over the land, angling across the ripples of ridges that rise on its eastern shore, and trying to stay out of the snow as much as I can. It is good to see the ground again after so many weeks. In the spots where the snow is entirely melted, the earth looks damp and tender from the intermittent freezing and thawing. It looks fresh and vulnerable, like a drowsy sleeper suddenly exposed by the covers being thrown back. There is still plenty of snow, though, in every vein and declivity in the earth.

I am headed back toward the cabin, and the afternoon cliff shadow has almost reached me when I look up and see a sundog, just one. It is a spectrumed halo of ice in an arc on the sun's south side. It lets me know the air above us is still crystalline.

Something has gone haywire with the plumbing in my work cabin, where our Christmas guests stayed, and none of our remedies have worked. This is no major crisis since the plumbing there will not be required till spring. But it is one of those nagging irritations that snag on the back of the brain, always making itself felt, interrupting repose. Will the line have to be dug up? The ground is frozen solid five feet down.

Along with this worry, we have been thinking a good deal about the spring. But we have no clear picture of it, cannot imagine ourselves in one place or another. Soon, within a few weeks, we will have to begin deciding, resolving.

I walk along the creek in the dusk which comes later enough in the day to be noticeable now. This is the time of day when the creek's surface turns opalescent, amethyst, pink, and purple, colors so slippery the eye is frustrated trying to pin them to a particular point. If one is up above the lake, looking down on it at this time, its whole surface swims in colors like this, reflecting the metamorphic sky. Earlier in the day, these water bodies were definite and dark. Only at evening do they begin their vacillating, unstable shifts of color, which, given another half hour, transmute to silver, then to pewter, and finally sink to gray again. People have always liked to watch this half hour or so when the light leaves the earth. The dying light transfigures the familiar.

So I walk along the creek, eying it, suspicious of its fleet instability, conscious of my fretful desire to hold it still so I can have it. There is this one opal evening and I can only have it now, at this moment. Like manna, it doesn't keep.

I try to memorize it, but the creek does not cooperate. It goes on sliding and shifting, growing grayer around the edges already. It doesn't care. Its ways are not my ways. It is imperious. It is time. The only vessel we have to catch its fluid in is memory, crystalline structures floating in the brain. Crystals and words, both of them structures pocked with spaces through which the colors leak, lost.

I turn back, defeated as I am every evening, and see a tunnel, slick in the snow, and reaching back into the bank. A weasel, or a marten, perhaps, lives here all the time and doesn't have to remember. He will be here in spring and, if he gets enough fish, next winter.

I climb up the bank and across the fence stile and down into the old smeared snow, hard as bones now. No one likes old dead snow that outstays its welcome.

So much of our days, so much of time, is made of litter—plugged-up sewers, dirty snow. We talk, with our leaky words and memories, as though life were made of decisions, plans, actions, moments of clear perceptions. But it's not. Clogged drains, desperation, unsatisfied hungers, sluggish snow melting at its own slack pace. How have we come to trim these pieces out of our descriptions of life? No wonder the world distrusts us Christians. The Jews had Job; we have Robert Schuller.

At night now I dream of impossible tasks being laid upon me. I am to ride a motorbike, something I've never done, and carry a loaded backpack at the same time. Or in another dream episode, I find myself in a stagy black wig, an opera score in my hands, trying to fake a performance. In the dream I do not feel exactly frantic, only scheming very hard as to how I can wing it.

And David, he has night terrors. He gets up and goes to the bathroom. I see the light on there between the logs and hear the caps coming off the medicine bottles. He comes back to bed and I feel him cold and untenanted against me. Some succubus is siphoning off his strength. I feel like Abishag. Soon he sleeps, hard and deep enough to snore.

I lie there and think about all the laughable formulas for life. At best they are like fingers we stick in the dike, to hold back chaos for a space, a very small space. We've even invented an architectural, Latinate language for the formulas: *decision, priorities, conflict management, self-actualization.* In the dark I see a vision of a thousand smug formula-fingers sticking from the muddy dissolving dike.

Where is our humility in the face of our actual situation? How can we ever cry anything but "Mercy!" in the middle of earth's long night?

The radio says the daffodils are blooming in Sweden. The grass is turning green in Oslo, and the Bay of Bosnia is free of ice. The false spring appears to be global, or at least hemispherical.

Here, four deer splash in the creek like sparrows in a birdbath. The beaver, not seen for a week or more, gnaws his willow withes as usual. But even he has noticed the fine weather. He takes a stick in his mouth and paddles across to a different rock. He affords himself a change of scene.

A rough-legged hawk has killed a rabbit right outside my study window.

As I came in this morning I heard a rustle under the dead tree by the creek bank. A cottontail scuttling away, I thought. Then I turned and saw some scrap of fur fly up among the rocks there. Later, I thought idly, I'll investigate.

But after I had built my fire and sat down at the window, I saw the hawk, large and hunch-shouldered over his prey, turning his head completely around, first one direction and then the other, mistrustfully. Raptors are mute on their hunting grounds. Their silence and their furtive, hunched stance as they knead their prey give them an air of guilty knowledge. One could almost pity them. At length the hawk flew off.

Suddenly the brittle branches of the dead tree under which the rabbit's body lay were filled with chickadees, flicking and bobbing and calling shrilly together. Was this a funerary congregation? Were they lamenting the ripped rabbit lying at the foot of their perch? Probably not. One flew to a strand of barbed wire just over the corpse. Was it curious? Was all their rabble-rousing a means of scolding or scaring the big, shifting, silent bird? Who knows?

Later I went and looked at the remains of the rabbit in broad daylight. There were two bright spots of blood on the snow, a wad of entrails full of the rabbit's own breakfast, and a cloud of fur as delicate as down. That was all. No hide, no head, no bones. How the hawk managed to make such a thorough job of it I don't know. His talons had taken away all but the offal.

Despite her open-air charnel house, earth is quite tidy and fastidious in these matters. There's hardly a gravy spot left when the creatures get through eating one another. A friend who has just come back from Yellowstone tells us how the coyotes there hang out with the bison in winter. The huge bison, swinging their shaggy heads from side to side, clear away the snow to get at the grass. In the process they uncover nests of mice who leap away in fright—right into the clutches of the waiting coyotes. Earth's economy is thus close-mortised and tenoned.

The magpies have discovered the leftover entrails of the rabbit that the hawk was too fine to take. Magpies are not too fine for anything. The name, in fact, is a shortened version of the original—"maggot-pie." There are at least four of them calling raucously over this unexpected picnic. They make a big to-do over their find. Unlike the mute predators, scavengers are loud and long-winded.

Nothing thaws today. We are sinking slowly into winter again, not plummeting as I had expected. No storm, no snow. Just the steady, gradual decrease in warmth.

In the afternoon I go out into the weak, diluted sunlight. Being tilted away from the sun as it is now, the hemisphere receives its light filtered through additional layers of mote-filled atmosphere. In summer, the rays will penetrate more directly and perpendicularly, but now we are merely grazed by photons. One can feel the very skin starving for them. And today the sun is further strained through a thin layer of ice crystals hanging higher up in the air.

I take one of those semiconscious walks where the mind, instead of maneuvering, merely follows where the feet lead. They lead through sagebrush to the point of fossil bed thrust up out of the valley floor about fifty feet into a wedge-shaped ridge. This sharp uplift of limestone is different from the surrounding moraines, which are made of rubble and rounded. In fact, the moraines are newcomers compared with the limestones.

Geologists have told us that this particular chunk of earth is millions of years old. Embedded in it are brachiopods, small shellfish from the Paleozoic period, and a few corals. Even up close, however, the layered ridge looks quite unextraordinary. It might have been made yesterday by an unskilled cement worker using inferior materials. The compacted dirt crumbles with surprising ease from around the fossils of which there are a profligate number. Visitors pocket them by the handfuls and nobody cares, there are so many. Despite their age, these antiques are hardly valuable.

Birds and small mammals have gouged out holes for themselves in the interstitial dirt and left their droppings there. Game trails lead over them; today's life forms ignore their humble ancestors. Or perhaps their seabed experience is simply incommunicable to these dry-land dwellers.

I, however, always feel an obligation to sit a spell among the mummies buried in this mass grave. They have outlasted Ramses himself. So what if they're the proletariat of the past and not Pharaoh? To touch them is to lay a finger on a world so foreign, so far in the past that it is almost mythic in time. What did *they* know of the world? What primeval knowledge is buried here among their fluted exoskeletons?

We use the mountains as a metaphor for constancy. We call them everlasting or eternal. But this is not so. Their changes may be slow, so slow as to mean nothing to us, but change they do. And, of course, the changes do mean a great deal to us and our history. The metamorphoses of earth's crust controls the politics of today. The buried bones of dinosaurs, of grass and trees and ferns, composted and compressed in the earth, giving off gases and turning to oily sludge, determine the dispersal of the world's armies today.

All this is accomplished by earth-death and the decay of the planet's skin—if one can use such dramatic terms for the slow sloshing up and down of the terrestrial minerals that form the earth's rind.

Geologists tell us that at the center of the earth lies a rigid core made of iron and nickel. Surrounding that hard inner heart is a fluid ring, made of the same minerals, but taking up more than a quarter of the earth's diameter. Over that fluid lies the mantle, a thick layer of rock in a plastic state, sometimes rigid under stress, often oozing and unstable. And over all this moiling of matters is stretched the comparatively thin skin of crust, which is all we know of the earth firsthand.

This crust, being of uneven depths, tends to slosh up and down. It only maintains any equilibrium at all because of equal and opposing movements that counterbalance each other. As the thick parts erode, they become lighter and the base underneath rises. At the same time, as the thin ocean bottoms accumulate debris, their bases sink under the weight, making them eventually thicker.

Orogeny—the birth of mountains—begins in the lowest depressions under the ocean. Sediments, whether from organic life, erosion of the continents, or minerals precipitating directly out of the seawater itself, build up to a depth of seven or eight miles. When the sediment gets this thick, its weight then pushes the underlying crust down, depressing it into the warmer regions of the mantle. The sediment becomes molten rock. Then it pushes up, blisterlike, shouldering aside older formations and younger sediment. The young mountain continues to rise. The old debris erodes and runs off its sides. Yet even as they are a-borning, they have started to die through the steady pressures of their own erosion.

Thus are mountains born, a properly long drawn-out process for the biggest things we know on earth. The pace varies a good deal, of course. A smallish mountain can be brought to birth from volcanic activity within a year or two, while the Rockies may have taken ten million years to rise.

But the death of mountains is always more drawn out than their birth. It will take the Rockies several times ten million years to wear away to lowly hills. The mountains here are mostly made of granite, which is a combination of feldspar and quartz. Feldspar is roughly as hard as steel and quartz is even harder. Mountain folk are notoriously conservative; perhaps they soak it up from their conservative surroundings, the cliffs and hogbacks and ridges so resistant to change.

Some of the core of the Rockies, uncovered by erosion, shows itself to be even older than the mountains themselves. Split Rock, Wyoming, southeast of here, a navigating point used by pioneers on the Oregon Trail, is a jumble of pre-Cambrian rock five times older than the mountains that surround it. It is a dinosaur even among mountains, an anachronism snagged somehow in a backwash in the up-and-down sloshing of the earth-rind. The rock has been exposed again to the air by erosion, like old bones turned up by a plow in a field.

We think that the earth never dies, but it does. At least these surface configurations so familiar to us as landscape appear and disappear over millennia. The psalmist took this long view when he wrote of the earth being removed and the mountains being carried into the midst of the sea. The mountain's manner of dying is so lengthy that it usually means little to us—until we have a fuel crisis. It is hard to comprehend that the sandstone cliffs across the road will someday be dust on the desert. But from my perch here on the wedge of shell-packed sediment I can hear segments fall and crash from the cliff face, a common sound during thawing and freezing cycles in winter. The noise echoes down the canyon like a rifle report.

All such downward movement of rock is called, technically, "degradation." The process includes the chemical attack on rock by atmospheric gases, moisture, and the acids from decomposing organic matter. Our mountains don't lose much to these attacks, however. They lose most of their substance to sheer temperature changes. The continual contraction and expansion these changes cause wears them worst. Their stony hearts do not expand and contract with ease. Also, water freezing in the cracks forces their mass apart. Such ice-prying exerts nearly two thousand pounds of expansive pressure per square inch on the rocks. And whatever plants manage to grow here are just as determined as the slower-witted stones. Trees will grow where there seems no soil at all. If their seed finds a moisture-collecting crevice, its fragile root hairs will eventually split the rock apart. And lichen, in green, yellow, orange, and black scabs, creeps across the stone's surfaces too, etching them with the acids of their own digestive processes.

But the mountains have more than these higher life forms and the temperature against them. They are broken down primarily by what geologists call "active agents"— water and wind. Not only do these wear away the rock, they also carry it away toward some distant desert or delta. It is not just the weight and motion of the water itself that rubs away the stones, but the suspended sediment it carries. Thus the mountain's own decomposing body is used against it like liquid emery.

The glaciers, those great frozen juggernauts that once scoured this valley, are driven back now into the mountain fastness, but even there they continue to gnaw at the topmost peaks, plucking boulders from the mountain turrets by freezing to the bedrock and dragging them loose, grinding the stone to rubble.

And then, of course, there is the wind, the constant saw grating through this tough earth-hide.

When all these destructive forces have done their worst, have chipped and pried and gouged loose great sheets and chunks of rock, then gravity takes over. Talus cones, huge hummocks made of the off-scouring of the mountains, are formed by mass-wasting, the descent of rubble toward the valley floors. These cones are the bane of mountain climbers and cross-country skiers. These heaps of debris are so unstable that a heavy snowfall or the spring melt or even a loud noise can sometimes break them loose from their base. Then they come crashing down in a sudden avalanche or a landslide.

The gneiss of which these mountains are made and the schist striped with needles of aluminous hornblende—some day their flecks of mica will be glinting from the bottom of a lowland streambed or be driving through the air warmed by a desert sun to greater degrees than anything they have known since they first oozed out onto the surface of the planet and crystallized among the glaciers.

It is such piling up of the debris of their death that leads finally to the making of new mountains. In fact, it's hard to tell where decomposition leaves off and gestation begins. Bury anything deep enough and it must come to life again, melted, reformed, given a new body, unrecognizable as its former self.

I was in Florence one summer, not long after the River Arno had flooded and eroded a good many of the city's famous artifacts. David, leaning over a crumbling balustrade, commented about the great age of the place, meaning, of course, not the place itself but the human history enacted upon it. For are not all places on earth of equal age? Isn't the planet coeval in all its parts, the iron core as well as the Wind River Mountains? Is not all dust, ours included, of the same generation? Only the shapes change, and the names by which we know them. The boundaries around entities are what shift. No telling where the chemicals that my own body can be reduced to came from. Under the ocean, on top of the Matterhorn. Maybe I've traveled more than I think.

Organic life has only speeded up considerably the up-and-down motion on this planet. Whereas mountains, with their sluggish mineral history, take millions piled upon millions of years to rise and die, trees, mice, and me take

only a moment. Put us under and we pop up again almost
as soon as we've rotted.

But mountains do things on a grand scale. In fact, scale
seems to be their whole point. The higher one rises, the
lower it falls and is buried. And the longer the length of its
decomposition-gestation.

Clouds, strange to say, have approximately the same
scale as mountains in space. They build to heights as high
as mountains and, obeying the same laws of compression
and heat, are eroded away by the wind, dispersing their
substance to start the entire process over again. But their
time-scale is radically different; they accomplish in hours
what it takes mountains millennia to do. But of course they
are mere ephemeral sketches of mountains. The water vapor
from which clouds are made is millions of times less dense
than the matter of mountains. Perhaps the time-scale of
cloud life is directly proportional to their density. At any
rate, if you would see a speeded-up version of mountain
building, look up on an afternoon when the sky is filled
with cumulus clouds.

Dante envisioned the apostles as mountains in Paradise,
towering over the rest of us. Purgatory too was a mountain
that one ascended as the load of sin became lighter. And
the Inferno was an upside down, negative-space mountain, a
geosyncline that fills and sinks with the debris of sinners,
who must, I suppose, be ground down and melted before
they can be uplifted again in whatever orogenic process
redemption demands. Perhaps it is not only flesh and
feldspar that needs this continual composting to achieve new
forms. Perhaps the spirit too necessarily undergoes its own
orogeny. Who knows what scale that demands, either in
time, in depth, or in density?

Third Sunday in Epiphany

Today Jesus stands up in the Nazareth synagogue and,
using Isaiah as his text, reveals himself as, at the least, a
prophet. And not a prophet of doom either, but of release
and recovery. The proverb that is fulfilled in Nazareth,
however, is the one about familiarity breeding contempt.
The hometown boy presumed too much. They tried to kill
him by throwing him over a cliff.

Why, I wonder, did he go out of his way to provoke

them so? Why was he intent on antagonizing his familiars from the beginning? Their initial reaction to him was gratifying enough. They spoke well of him and were amazed at his gracious words, the text says. So why did he keep on needling his good neighbors there in the synagogue? Why couldn't he leave well enough alone? Why did he have to make all those sarcastic remarks about Elijah and the foreign widow and Elisha healing the leprous Gentile general? Did he intentionally provoke an incident? Was he an inside agitator? A suicidal maniac bent on martyrdom?

Maybe he wanted to get things straight from the start, to skip the honeymoon period with the folks back home who would inevitably brag about the prophet they had produced. Maybe he wanted everyone to understand from the beginning that his destiny was a dangerous one. For with Isaiah's words of healing and hope in his mouth it would have been easy to puff him as a positive thinker, a problem-solver.

Sometimes it seems that if there were any way for Jesus to offend people, he would find it. Pharisees, scribes, priests. His mother and brothers. The pig-farmers of Gadara. Cashiers and sheep-dealers in the Jerusalem temple. Peter. Martha of Bethany. The sole conciliatory gesture he made was directed toward the Baptizer after he had been imprisoned and was alone and confused about this strange, enigmatic figure for whom he was sacrificing his head, the one about whom he had made such extravagant public claims.

John's message from prison, sent through his disciples to Jesus, has always struck me as the most poignant question in all the Scriptures: "Are you he who is to come, or shall we look for another?" A whole lifetime is contained in those words. Years of abnegation, sacrifice, zealous aberrations lived out on sheer nerve. And he only wants to know, from the horse's mouth, if it has all been to some point, of some worth, or if it has been as vain as water poured out on the desert sand.

Jesus, replying to the one who will go before him in death as he has preceded him in life, again uses the same Scripture he had read that day in the Nazareth synagogue. By now Isaiah's prophecy of healing and hope had been fulfilled. And Jesus attaches to it an almost pleading admonition to his cousin: *Blessed is he who takes no offense at me.*

Perhaps it is only in such extreme circumstances as John's, imprisoned and on the point of death, that anyone is vouchsafed even this answer. Jesus, who at times went out of his way to offend people, was anxious that this one not be offended. He was at pains that this Epiphany, sent secondhand, should be inoffensive and efficacious. While John's messengers are still within earshot, he delivers his eulogy to John, calling him Elijah.

This Elijah was not, however, to be swept up to heaven by a passing chariot. John had prepared the way of the Lord by preaching in the wilderness. Now he prepares the way of the Lord by going before him into death. Not a death from natural causes, but by execution for offending Herod. A death that might have been avoided by a little politic placation. The same kind of death that lies ahead for the messiah.

We most often think of incense and the three kings at Epiphany, but Epiphany came to John in prison. Either way, Epiphany always has some inevitable connection with death. The magi themselves before they left for the East again must have heard the wailing mothers of the slaughtered infants. And even in the Nazareth synagogue, it was only the work of a moment to turn the hearers' hearts from pride in their hometown boy to his murder. Divine revelation seems to provoke human retaliation. No wonder God hides himself so much. On those occasions when he shows himself, he invites our attack. It makes you wonder if we really want to know him.

We go up on Arrow Mountain today with our ornithologist friend. We hear nuthatches and pine siskins *zreeing* and *nyahing* in the tall Douglas fir. See elk tracks and droppings in the snow. Wade through more drifts than we had expected to find on the trail. At the top we sit huddled behind boulders from the wind and hurriedly eat dried apricots and drink tea, passing the thermos with stiff fingers. David climbs further up the trail and discovers a whole herd of bighorns.

On the way down, almost home, the ornithologist's dog gets caught in a coyote trap along the creek. David is able to free the animal before it's damaged too badly.

Coyotes, however, must chew off their own foot to escape. Most of them freeze to death first. The trapper carries a noose to choke the animal in case it is still alive when he comes to check his traps. This season, trappers are getting $35 a head for a killed coyote.

A death in the family. We get the message two days after the event. I drive David to the airport in the afternoon and see him off.

The man who died would have been ninety next month. He is not a close relative of David's. There is little personal grief. But he was nevertheless a peg in a complex loom of family relationships. With his sudden death, important cords in the fabric have been cut loose. Living arrangements will necessarily be altered. A home must be disposed of. People's lives resettled. Where death invades, there are always refugees to be resettled. Homes broken up, belongings packed away, people deposited in unfamiliar settings.

I drive back up the canyon in the dark, alone, and near the cabin, catch a mule deer in my headlights. His antlers are like a bare tree, its branches stylized and symmetrical. He crosses the road in front of me warily but without hurry.

I unload the groceries and laundry from the car in broad moonlight, then come out by the woodpile one more time, my arms hanging and unhampered, to see the sky. The canyon rims hold the moon's brimming luminescence like a bowl. The sky is a huge, pale fish-eye, and the moon, hazed by cataracts, is the pupil. It stares down at me and at the coyotes and at the cottontails hiding in the woodpile. When I go to bed I hear an owl calling to the enormous eye.

A storm, they say, is coming from California.

Well, the storm never amounted to more than clouds and wind. Further south there was snow, but only about half an inch fell here yesterday morning and that was gone by the time I got back from church. Such small amounts of snow often do not melt here. The temperature is not above freezing. The snow simply gets sucked up into the dry air straight from its frozen state.

It is raining in California, the Riverton radio station tells me. Houses are descending into the ocean. But here there is no movement. I am held by a clock that does not tick. Every day is like the one that went before.

January and February are dry months here. There will be more snow, but it will come in the spring, heavy and thick and wet. In Wyoming, snow is a sign of spring, a sign of life. A sacrament of hope held in moisture. But for now, the earth is dry and brittle. When I go out to walk, it is a trip through a charnel house and does not lift the heart.

A good bit of the ground is exposed now. It looks gray and dull and lusterless. What snow is left lies like calcified bones on top of the ground, hard and unyielding, dirty and drear. The uncovered ground is a chaos of coarse dirt and rock bits. It is not even ground fine enough to be called soil. Gray and dun are the only colors. Not snuff, not russet, not bronze or fawn; not even tan. But only leaden, drab, dingy, ashen gray and dun. The evergreens no longer stand out against it. The very vacuum of these uncolors leach away the trees' darker streaks on the slopes.

It is the end of January, and I suppose a good many people all over the Northern Hemisphere are tasting the ashes of the world in their mouths. Even if they are unconscious of the cause, they feel a weariness of the spirit stealing over them. They get restive and maybe fly to Florida or the Caribbean. Looking for a little unlocal color. Anything but this everlasting, unchanging deadness of gray and dun. I stick it out here in the wilderness, alone still except for the cat, but I don't enjoy it. The drama that brought the earth's death has gone now. All that's left is looking at the corpse, day after day.

I hike up to the falls, a place that a month ago was mantled in subtle green ice. Now its folds have been worn down by the early January thaw, the colors tarnished with debris. It looks as shopworn as the snow bones littering the land around the cabin.

But, of course, I didn't come here to enjoy death. I didn't want to catch only the first act, full of drama and change. Change, one way or another, is always intriguing and beguiles our attention, keeps us awake. When the world stops changing is when it really dies. And death in the end may simply be boring.

I don't know where the Greeks got the idea that immutability was an attribute of divinity. Perhaps because they lived in a warmer climate and never wintered over in Wyoming.

Immutability and chaos seem to be the twin dangers to consciousness, attacking it from opposite sides. Chaos is a hot swirl of unsociated scraps in which our own perception cannot find a reflection. A cold unchangeableness, on the other hand, frustrates our always mobile organism. We participate in what we perceive. And to participate in immutability is to die, to slow down, screech, stumble, and finally freeze into the same stasis we see.

This is death. Not just the heart of darkness but the heart of stasis, catatonic and surd. Unvarying, unchanging. The Platonists and Nirvana-lovers can have it, this immutability worship. How can the living God live at absolute zero? The Hebrew God weeps, rages, smites, repents, exults, gathers. He at least has a story line. Which is not to say that he is diminished by his changes. On the contrary, he continually effloresces, sprouts new tendrils, blooms, gives birth. Manifests himself in all incarnated possibilities. Among them, death.

Which is why I still go out and crunch across the ossified snowdrifts, sit among the cold tombstones. It makes my very guts ache. My sight is nothing but a burden. My eyes are scurvied over with stasis. Even the sound of the ravaging wind would be welcome now. One gets to the point, the very edge of the abyss, of cursing this unchanging earth.

It is even past the point of passive diminishment now. Diminishment is at least movement, even if movement downward. I chunk a stone into the lake, just to hear a plop.

It is here, now, when the nerves are exacerbated by nothingness and the daily repetition of nothingness, that one feels most intensely the desire for life. The longing, acrid and fusty on the tongue, for one sign of life. I feel like Dives, praying for a single drop of water from Lazarus in Abraham's teeming bosom. Snowflakes falling, wind thrashing and heaving the trees. Any drop will do. (How easily we forget, the rest of the year, this end-of-January anguish.)

There is one moment, one only, of the day that is different. Early in the morning, at about a quarter to seven now, the moment happens. I get up early and build a fire so that I can be at the window to catch it. Nothing else happens the rest of the day. Only this moment happens. It occurs when the light is coming. The gray then is not ashen but expectant. The world stretches up, holds out its arms in the absolute stillness. The stillness itself is alive for a moment, alive to waiting. At the height of the moment it makes a single piercing cry. Then quickly, as the cumbersome winter light increases and the echo dies away, it falls back again and is lost. That's it. Nothing happens the rest of the day. But tomorrow I will get up and build my fire early so I can hear—and make—that cry.

February

In the afternoon I go up to the shale cliffs at the trailhead. Their south and east slopes lie exposed to the sun so that most of the snow has melted from them and the walking is easier there.

On the road up to the cliffs I meet a large herd of bighorn sheep. One of the rams stands on a rock about fifteen feet from me. His great eye looks as weary of winter as I am. A nearby ewe has the fixed stare of a hysterical mountain woman shut up by weather too long. Only the yearlings among them have much spunk left.

They cross the road in front of me at a desultory amble. All they've had to eat for some time now is the sere bunchgrass, and they're beginning to look ragged and motley. One ewe walks with a rickety, off-center gait; her coat is patchy where hunks of the long winter hair have come loose. A yearling follows her, his own coat dark and ratty, his face as ugly as a camel's. These are the ones the coyotes will get. Or disease. Whoever can't stand up to the long winter diet of deprivation. Now, in this long, lean stretch before the first new grass sprouts, the weak are going to sicken and die. Last year an epidemic of pink-eye spread through Wyoming's bighorn sheep population. It was first noticed by the government biologists when the animals began unaccountably falling over cliffs.

By winter's end, seventy to ninety-five percent of Wyoming elk will be carrying lungworm parasites. Tularemia will afflict rabbit warrens where the animals are crowded together underground.

It has not been an exceptionally hard winter for wildlife here in this canyon. Although their forage was pretty well covered during December when they had to rake out patches of grass from under the snow or nibble the thin leaves of rabbitbrush, by mid-January half the slopes and most of the valley floor were clear again. Three years ago we had deep snow from Thanksgiving on. I traveled across the southern border of the state by train that April and saw scores of antelope carcasses where they had dropped, driven up against fence rows they were too weak and starved to cross.

This year they are luckier. Few will actually starve to

death. But the weak ones will sicken and die, either directly from the effects of malnutrition or indirectly from attacks of predators.

I had heard a coyote cry at midmorning. It startled me to hear that sound so unexpectedly in broad daylight. I wondered if it had not been caught in a trap itself.

This afternoon, from the top of the shale cliffs, I saw the coyote's predator. He left his pickup parked in the road while he went down to the creek to check his traps. The truck was there a long time. I spent a good while picking at the shale with my fingers. It came loose in leaves, like the crumbling pages of an old, decayed book. The pickup was gone when I came down again.

Tonight I hear on the radio that a man in the Midwest has been fined for setting a fox free from a trap where it would have frozen to death or starved. In this world, death has the prerogatives.

Groundhog Day

In this part of the country, anything remotely resembling a groundhog is still asleep. We don't have true groundhogs in Wyoming, but its close cousin, the yellow-bellied marmot, lives among the talus cones or fans of rock debris that spill down from mountain sides. The marmots are sometimes called rockchucks, a name that shows their kinship to the eastern woodchuck or groundhog.

Marmots have a problem here in the mountains, however. While the groundhog can dig its tunnels up to five feet deep and thirty feet long in the soil-rich meadows of the East and ride out the winter in snugness, our marmots can only make relatively shallow shelters in the rocks. Thus a good many of them freeze to death during hibernation, unless the snow falls deep enough to insulate them well. If the marmot survives, it may be out by next month, an early riser among hibernators. Right now he lies in his stony sepulchre, breathing only once every six minutes, his heart muscle contracting only once every fifteen seconds. That's passive diminishment for you.

In yesterday's mail came news of three deaths. A friend's mother has died suddenly. A first child has died soon after birth. And another friend's thirty-year-old daughter was accidentally shot a few days before Christmas.

There are just as many deaths as there ever were in the world, despite our vague assurance that things are different now, that people don't die like they used to. The death rate is still a hundred percent. It's going on around us all the time. We just don't pay attention. We have devised ways to divert our attention.

Even if I could visit my bereaved friends, there would be no body there to mourn over. Nor would the death have been, even for a day, the central fact in the communities in which they live. A notice, perhaps, appeared in the newspaper. The funeral procession stopped traffic at intersections but purposefully avoided the center of town. And that was all. After they had passed, the traffic started up again. Death sank below the surface. It scarcely left a dent on the business above ground.

We may shrug off these occasions, like momentary stutters in the engine of our forward movement, but it has not always been so. The practice of embalming bodies was not common in this country until well after the Civil War. Until then, death was a community, rather than a commercial effort. Neighbors came to lay out the body, washing and dressing it in the clothes bought or saved especially for the occasion. While they waited for the carpenter to construct the coffin, often from planed boards that had been stored in the attic, the body was laid out on a cooling board in some unheated room. If the weather permitted, it was frozen on the back porch. The Pennsylvania Dutch even built a special room in their homes called a *doed-kammer* for keeping the corpse till burial. Invitations to the funeral were sent out, either oral or written. Church bells tolled. The body was carried to the cemetery on an open wagon or sleigh or, if the graveyard was a family plot near to hand, on the shoulders of the bearers.

Afterward there were funeral feasts. In fact, weddings and funerals provided the primary social occasions for most communities well into this century. Casks of wine were often put away at the birth of a child to be opened either for its wedding or its funeral, whichever came first. If for the wedding, then some of the same stock was held over for the funeral, a liquid link of continuity running from one end of life to the other. And the cask sat there stolidly through the years, a reminder of the inevitable occasion on which it would be tapped. There were even special kinds of foods that ethnic groups concocted especially for funerals. Dutch funeral feasts always featured *leicht boi,* a raisin pie. It meant death, the way turkey means Thanksgiving or fruitcake means Christmas.

In fact, funerals became such lavish social affairs that in 1721 the Massachusetts Bay Colony passed a law forbidding the giving of expensive gifts to the participants in the ceremony as mementos of the dead. Gloves and rings were the usual tokens. The pastor of Boston's Old North Church received a total of 2,940 pairs of funeral gloves during his thirty-two years of service there. Samuel Sewell, one of the Salem judges, acquired fifty-seven mourning rings from those who had gone before. A goodly portion of the deceased's estate often went to pay the funeral bills. Early Americans were so concerned to go out in style that both before and after the Revolutionary War, fines were levied against lavish funeral spending in order to prevent unnecessary bankruptcies.

Compared with our ancestors, our own funerals are shabby, shame-faced, hole-in-a-corner affairs. No gifts are bestowed, certainly, other than anonymous donations to medical funds and some flowers. And a few melting Jello salads, a canned ham, a cake mix serve to feed the mourners. We're lucky if we can assemble our far-flung families for the funeral and a few friends can get off from work to attend the twenty-minute service.

When was the last time you saw a dead body? Or touched one? Even an animal's body? Nothing else in this world compares with that experience for teaching mystery. Body-viewings and open-casket funerals are, I realize, out of fashion now. But all you have to do, whatever your measure of sophistication or gentility, is look down at a face in a coffin to be staggered by the sudden foreignness of the familiar. The absolute unreachableness of the person you spoke to perhaps only yesterday.

Or take up the limp, still-warm body of a cat. One can feel through the fingers the sudden vacancy, the fleet going. A moment ago it was there; now it is manifestly not-there. A hole has opened in the universe that has not quite closed over again, and through it you can feel, rushing past, a slight wind.

We don't see death firsthand much anymore. This gives our watching it on television or seeing it in magazine photographs a certain quality of voyeurism. A coupling of disgust with a furtive fascination. Yet we certainly don't touch it. And thereby we lose at once both the mystery and the matter-of-factness.

Six below zero two mornings in a row. Barely up to zero by ten. Another half inch of snow, which evaporates without ever melting. The hard, dry, diamondlike snow that comes in January and February. It glistens on the ground in huge, extended crystals, striking blue and green and red shards of light into the unwary eyeball from the sagebrush. But glistening is about all it's good for. At least this is the opinion of the livestock people hereabouts. It holds scarcely any moisture to feed their fields. But I find it convenient to have a fresh fall like this when I go hiking. I can scrape a handful off a rock or from the top of the old bony snow and eat it instead of carrying a canteen. Yet this snow, formed in the supercooled upper atmosphere, is practically as dry as dust and it takes several scrapings to get the equivalent of a sip of water.

The freshly formed ice on the creek is different now too. It grows long needles, maybe two inches long, which protrude both vertically and horizontally from the edges of the old ice. The needles look like the long fibers in muscles.

When I go out on the porch at midafternoon, ready for a brisk walk in the cold, crystal air, I shake out the fiber doormat and find, concealed there, a deer mouse, flattened and frozen stiff. There is it. Death at my doorstep. How many times already have I trod on it unwittingly, hidden there in the fold of the mat?

I hold up the stiff little body by its long naked tail. The long winter coat is gray mottled with bright amber and brown with white underneath. The legs are splayed out, the tiny toes marvelously delicate and floral. The fine, velvety ears are folded backward against the head like crushed flower petals. On its white underside I see clearly the red indentions made by my cat's teeth. Like most domesticated killers, she never eats her prey. When the sport is over, she delivers it with a fastidious nicety to the front door. I had thought by now she had cleared the place entirely. This must be the remains of some foolhardy or desperate latecomer who bumbled into her territory.

I turn it by the tail once more to memorize it, then sling it out and down the slope in front of the cabin where the magpies will find it tomorrow.

Returning from the ridge later in the afternoon, I spy nine mule deer, does and yearlings together. They disport themselves with considerably more sprightliness than the sheep; they are more wary and less lethargic. Winter hasn't been as hard on them. For one thing, they herd together in fewer numbers and thus have more forage and less disease. Also this is their natural habitat, while the sheep are forced into the canyon from higher altitudes.

The deer saw me only a moment after I had spotted them. They held their heads erect and their large ears were quivering. They only stared a few seconds before bounding up the next rise in their peculiar jackrabbity run, all four legs leaping at once. This kind of leaping run is called, I have discovered, "stotting." They went with the day's bounding blue sky.

The light is noticeably stronger now, with almost half an hour extra tacked on to each end of the day. The Absorakas look, against their background, not blue enough to be called cobalt, but bright enough for, say, a man's shirt. And clear, as if they had been cut out with a razor and straightedge.

I go back to the cabin and the cat at sundown. I have been by myself for over a week now and have another one to go. I lie on the bed and stare at the skeletal ribs rising around me, the round logs like the inside of Jonah's whale.

I like it that way. I even like the murdered mouse on the doormat. I throw more tree bones on the fire to warm myself. They remind me daily that I *owe* my life. I am in debt to death. Could not live without it. The cosmos is my creditor, one whose accounts always balance—eventually. Without these reminders I am liable to get uppity. To think that my life comes to me new-minted, a currency that needs no capital to back it. That I am the world's wealth created out of nothing. But not so. By the time I die, a good portion of the earth will have given its life for me. Then it will be my time to make myself useful.

I nearly lost my nerve today. Maybe being alone for two weeks had something to do with it. You work along, carefully or desperately as the day demands, snatching, balancing, luring words into position, when suddenly, without any warning, it all falls flat. The whole house of cards slumps and sprawls apart, and the only objective, rational response seems to be "So what?"

I had been writing about a young girl in 1944, a girl of no particular importance to anyone but me. Why am I so intent on catching her precisely as she comes down the stairs or stands by the window crying? She probably doesn't even remember this herself. She was unaware that my child's eyes were fixed on her and, forty years later, are desperate to disgorge that burden on paper. Another forty years and both of us will be gone. So what.

In the afternoon I go up to the deserted library and let myself in to the frigid cabin. I only just manage not to be overwhelmed by the uneven ranks of books because I am familiar with them from months of browsing. Still, the print, the words, the very letters of the alphabet seem oppressive. I pull a picture book off the lower shelf; it's the only thing I can stomach today.

It is one of those oversized history-of-art books with a coarse-textured fabric cover. Carefully avoiding the text, I turn the pages over, landing with a flick of my finger among the T'ang Dynasty, the Japanese warlords, Celtic dragons. Hey, this is great. I am suddenly seeing the world with someone else's eyes. What a burden it takes from my own. I can almost feel my optic nerves quivering with relief.

I turn another page. A Greek girl, a little green from time and with her nose chipped away, glances obliquely from the page. But, oh, the hair, braided in a coronet around the face. The large eyes hiding her peculiar cause for delight, her mouth lopsided in a knowing but ample smile. Obviously, there had been a model for this girl. She is not stylized. Her particular charm rests in the sculptor's effort to capture a swift expression, a fleeting onceness. This piece of hammered-on stone—no, not even that—this mere photograph of a piece of wrought stone makes me, with jarring suddenness, love girls again, love that being of humans young, female, and secretive. And even makes me, through her, as through a crystal lattice that filters the light aimed from behind it into my eye, love God. She might have been no more than a girl passing in the street, but so manifest, so veritable, that she staggered the watcher. And still, ages after, she remains an epiphany of a girl.

Even so, it was not till later, walking back in the cold twilight from the library, that it comes to me, why I worked so hard to catch my own 1940s girl. She too was one of those crystals, falling everywhere about us as thick as snow, disappearing almost as soon as formed, but aiming the beam her singular construction sieved from that otherwise inaccessible light shining from behind her.

No change in the weather. Only the same cold, the same stillness, the same dead, unburied snow that chokes the paths and hiking trails. One would welcome even a windstorm now. At least there would be something to listen to, something to rasp and beat on the tympanic membrane. I talk to the cat just to have a sound in the house. She looks at me in vague disgust and goes back to sleep. She has a means of sinking into a vegetative state that I have not attained.

Virginia Woolf said she wrote to a rhythm rather than a plot. But this is no rhythm. This is only a caesura we have fallen into and don't know how to climb out of again. A full stop that has faltered and can't somehow strike the next beat. Silence and sameness and unthawing cold.

I feel like the Gerasene demoniac who lived among the tombs. "Night and day among the tombs and on the mountains he was always crying out, and bruising himself with stones."

Well. I can understand that. Give me another two weeks of this unremitting nothing and I would be in his shape. The boulders I pass are like tombs. I wander among them like a dejected survivor shut up in a cemetery. The canyon itself is like a trench dug for some immense grave. I could shriek at the ribs of rock that rise up on both sides of me except that the silence would swallow the sound and leave the air stiller than before.

It's easy to understand the madman's cries and even his scraping himself with stones. It is the same form of madness engendered in those submersion tanks where the subject is deprived of all sensory stimuli, of all change. Sunk in water heated to body temperature, blindfolded and deprived of sound, he feels only his own pulse, his own inner rumblings. After a while he begins to hallucinate. Legion sprouts in his suffocated brain. He would gladly rake his own flesh at such a time for some assurance of reality outside his own skull. Sensory deprivation is Descartes' world, not mine. It makes demoniacs of us all. And even the demons pleaded to be delivered from the nothingness of disembodiment, the death of senses. Better a pig's snuffling and grunting and limited vision than no body at all.

I have learned another aspect of death: it does not end with the Passion. God knows there is drama enough in that, when the cry of dereliction can still be made. But pain is only a prelude to death. As long as the demoniac could still cry out among the tombs and bruise himself with the stones, he was not yet quite dead. Even the demons did not know death until they plunged headlong over the abyss.

We've had a lot of romancing death in our era.

Hemingway with his melancholy bullfighters; Emily Dickinson with her gentlemanly coachman; Walt Whitman and his lilacs blooming by the dooryard. But the one who would show death accurately must present us with a blank page to stare at for a long, long time, allowing no deviation, no alternation of the surface, until our eyes stop perceiving, our mind doesn't know itself to be seeing, indeed, doesn't know itself at all. Death is not La Belle Dame sans Merci. Death is a squealing pig striking the surface of the abyss, consciousness extinguished from its desperate eyes.

It is that ultimate horror of all consciousness: entropy, nothingness, frozen stillness. It is the final ring in Dante's Hell—the frozen lake. To be forced to stare forever at nothing. Compared with this, flames, any suffering is preferable.

Vacuity is creation's death, or its closest approach in this world. No wonder it groans, adding its voice to the demoniac's. Absolute zero lies at the bottom of its abyss, that temperature at which all molecular motion stops. The point at which it no longer is constantly transformed from one configuration to another. From a fish to an otter, from water and sunlight to energy, leaf to bacterial body, phenomenon to phenomenon. At absolute zero it stops, freezes, ceases altogether.

Certain Eastern texts tell us that this is in fact the state of blessedness, this suspension of phenomenon and the dissolution of the consciousness that beholds it. My canyon is amenable to such an enterprise just now.

I, on the contrary, find that I am not really in love with death itself. This unremitting blankness holds no spiritually erotic possibilities for me. There is nothing alluring about it. I cannot aim myself at unbeing, at absolute zero. I can submit to death, but I do not love it. I can enter it, but only because it is the way to what I love.

And winter, our seasonal analogue for death, a mere memento of the real thing, is enough to turn me into a Gerasene demoniac, howling for a little life among the entombed world, whetting myself against the cold stones.

I don't go out looking for anything at all when I walk now. I only walk for my health, wretched thought. As though health of one's soul and body could be divorced from the state of the earth one walks upon. As though the road, the frozen lake, the valley were not reflected in my own interior. The world's sap is sunk and so is mine. The world is a great weariness I bear just by opening my eyes on it.

People in towns have the expedient, at this stage of winter, of finding life in the interchange of energy that society engenders. This is the season of concerts, plays, courses of study. This is when the Wyoming legislature meets—during the forty-two days following the new year's festivities. The human enterprise keeps itself going now by feeding on its own inventions, not by what it draws from the land, which, like an old dry cow, has nothing more to give.

And I, alone here, have the sole society of my cat, a few Shakespeare recordings, and the news twice a day on the radio. A lean enough meal, though I manage to dole it out so as to make it last.

In fact, I do better with the mind's meals than with the body's. Food itself has lost its meaning. I only eat for my health, in the same way I walk now. My heart isn't in it. The toast and eggs lie there on the plate, a necessity and no more. I had not realized that eating by oneself was such a trial. I think up little treats to tempt my appetite. But no good. I find the avocado, eaten alone, is no more than the equivalent of the eggs. They are both just so much bulk to get inside one's gullet. Tube-feeding, injections directly into the veins, would be just as tasty, mean just as much.

It surprises me how much communion is a part of meals. Pass the salt, we say to one another, meaning pass me your soul, pass me your self. Only that seasoning gives us heart to eat. Let me behold your eyes, eyes lit from behind like icons, and then I can swallow, can savor. Take away the eyes, and the food turns to ashes in the mouth, just so much fodder to be crammed and processed through the mechanism of the gut. Food and drink demand a mediating presence to truly nourish. Those who eat always alone, how do they do it? How do they sustain life? It's not just hot meals the old and sick need delivered to their doorstep, but the hand that holds the salt.

Perhaps this is why I no longer look when I walk either. Sometimes seeing requires someone else to say "Look!" Or at least it requires the knowledge that at evening you can say, "Guess what I saw."

So I tramp on down the valley floor, noting with jaded palate only those things that force themselves on my attention. A small herd of sheep that stop and stare at me across the road. Elk droppings and tracks on the far side of the creek. I watch for traps too, determined, if I come across one, to sink it in the deepest hole under the ice I can find.

There is a spot where the water is running free and shallow over round stones. It is a small but lovely sight and I stop to soak it in. The light catches and moves on the ripples. Liquid light movement. It eases the aching of my eyes for a moment after miles of dun dirt and bleared snow. Then I notice something else in this shallow swiftness. A school of fingerlings, four and five inches, nosing against the current. A small sight, but enough for delight to snag on.

I can scarcely separate the small fish from their stoney bed, the colors are so close, that speckled gray-green and gold. If David were here, he'd be able to tell their kind. Brook trout or brown or rainbow. These fingerlings are his herald. Tomorrow, tomorrow night, he comes home and I can eat again.

We get back from the airport, eighty miles away, after dark. Go in, build a fire, and feast on pickled herring, pralines, and sherry.

Last Sunday in Epiphany

Down on the Wind River Reservation they are celebrating the one hundredth anniversary of the mission church there. John Roberts, a Welshman and an Episcopal priest, arrived there during the winter of 1883, one of the coldest on record. The 150-mile trip up from the train stop in Green River took eight days. It was so cold that even the commercial stage was not running. The young missionary from Wales, who had requested an assignment among the wildest Indians America had to offer, made his way north in −60° temperatures with the U.S. mail clerk.

This winter has not been nearly that hard along the Wind River. The skies are heavy today, but as we pick our way among the aspen and the apple trees in the little orchard that Roberts planted around his two-room cabin and the log church, the clumps of snow are melting. The cabin is used as a storeroom for old and broken furniture now. Plaster has crumbled from the lathes on the walls inside. In a handmade desk we find some of Roberts's own books. The log church is in good repair, however. It is often used, we are told, for weddings by people who come out to the reservation from Lander.

In the large two-story stone building, the one that served as the school for Shoshoni girls during Roberts's day, the women of the mission church are serving dinner to all the visitors. Roast beef, baked potatoes, Indian fried bread. On the long tables are plastic pitchers of coffee and Kool-Aid. The women serve with the same deft lack of nonsense one finds at any church dinner.

The long tables are filled with visiting clergy and their families, young Shoshoni and Arapaho couples no longer living on the reservation, and kids. The one across from me might be twelve. She is wearing a pink T-shirt that shows a smirking cartoon cat. Under the cat is a caption that says, "I'm innocent." David tries some funny comment as one does with junior-high kids, but she turns her head away awkwardly. The food may be familiar, but the conversational style is not.

Afterward we wander through other rooms in the old school, looking at the displays of old photographs from the Roberts period of the mission. His saddle is also there, and beside it, a video-cassette player running scenes from various western movies that have been filmed on the reservation. No one is watching the video; its sole significance seems to be in the mere fact of its presence.

The afternoon service is held in the present church building. The pews are already packed and we sit along the back wall on folding chairs. This building is log, too, but a good many times larger than Roberts's original chapel. Except for the buckskin paraments and the cables and turnbuckles stretched from wall to wall as extra braces against the weather, it might be any somewhat seedy rural church in America.

The bishop, who has flown his own plane into Lander for the afternoon service, paces in the vestibule, waiting for things to get under way. His gold cape makes a little territory around him. Finally, the processional begins. The local vicar follows the bishop in his obviously homemade alb.

Besides the regular surging up and down of the congregation for the hymns, lessons, prayers, there is the backwash, the little eddies of toddlers or mothers with infants moving toward the back door and up the aisle again. An undercurrent of nursery noises out of which the voices of the readers and celebrants rise like waves.

Intermittently, an Indian man with a guitar sings. I wonder if he is blind; he wears dark glasses and aims his stare at the opposite wall. The songs he sings are not from the Episcopal liturgy. They are more familiar to me than that. They are the songs that belong to the poor church of whatever persuasion. "Jesus walked this lonesome valley ..." The rhythm is slightly, subtly altered. "Ere you left your room this morning," strum, strum, extra pause, "did you think to pray?" It is the plaintive mode of the psalms. *This poor man cried ... How long, O Lord, how long?* One does not hear that peculiar mournful note from the advocates of the poor, but only from the poor themselves. Those who feel themselves to be creeping across the deep sea bed over which others flash in the upper atmosphere with seemingly effortless ease. The poor have a dogged manner of insisting on their own experience.

As soon as the singer is finished, the vicar picks up hurriedly and without comment. Someone is standing and reading from the pew now about the pillar of fire, about Moses coming down from the mountain with his face shining. It strikes me that this story must not sound nearly as strange to the Shoshonis as it does to suburbanites. They had a Moses themselves and not long ago—Washakie, for whom the town here is named. Like Moses, his original connections to the tribe are shrouded. He came from outside. He was, however, such a good leader, so courageous in dealing with neighboring enemy tribes, and so shrewd in dealing with the invading whites that he saved the Shoshonis from extinction. He too lived in his camp up on the mountain above the fort where he felt himself to be closer to the cosmic action.

Despite Roberts's efforts, despite his schools and acts of mercy, the conversions among the Shoshonis were negligible. He and Washakie had a fine friendship, but the chief had no interest in becoming a Christian. Three years before his death, his favorite son was killed down in the fort in a barroom brawl. Washakie, quite old by then, sent word that he was coming down from the mountain to avenge his son's death. He promised to shoot every white man he came across until he himself was killed. The little Welshman heard this, got on his horse, and rode up the mountain to the chief's camp. He told Washakie he had come to die for the son's murder. It was in the early hours of the January morning that the chief was baptized.

Later, the gospel is read, the account of the Transfiguration. Again, the shining face on the mountain. Again I sense the ease with which the scene sluices into the apprehension of the people around me; the barriers that our own acculturation sets up to the gospel are not here. The Transfiguration is not a strange story to the Shoshonis the way it is to us. Of course. It is perfectly obvious to go up on the mountain for certain metamorphic experiences. It's what you expect. On the mountain one is joined by those figures who participate in the world's strong medicine. Whatever abstractions of thought we may be able to weave about this scene, there is a physical comprehension of its reality in this particular sanctuary that is lacking in downtown Denver.

After the gospel follows the confirmation of about two dozen youngsters, dressed in their best. Polyester Levis for the boys, wooden platform high heels for the girls. One of the confirmands and his father take up the collection. Already the boy is as large as the man. His long arms stick several inches below the wristband of his white shirt, the cuff too small to button.

The bishop preaches. The vicar reads a congratulatory letter from one of Roberts's daughters, now living in a nursing home in California. The stalk to the altar to receive communion begins. Once again there is that same shyness, that characteristic holding back among the Indians. The line does not move as fast as at the church where I go every Sunday. The bishop has taken off both his cope and his collapsible miter. It is very warm up near the altar. The old woman next to me at the rail has an aluminum cane and is tied up in a scarf like a Russian granny.

Then it is over and we are outside in the welcome cool air. The visiting clergy are making obligatory ecclesiastical jokes to one another. The bishop scurries past, his costume in a plastic valet bag, eager to get airborne before the snow starts. Everyone is saying the service was "wonderful," "beautiful," "lovely." The Indians are melting away.

It is good we had the sacrament to share.

It starts to snow on the way home and continues through the night. A heavy, damp blanket of snow. And this night a man on the reservation kills himself. "Self-inflicted hanging," as the Riverton radio station puts it. The vicar will conduct a litany at his home before the interment at the Sacajawea cemetery.

The Shoshonis came into this part of the Rockies only sporadically at first from the Great Basin area on the western side of the Rockies. There they had been root and seed gatherers and had hunted small game. By spring they were usually in a state of near starvation and so weak that they were easy prey for the Utes who raided their small camps. The Utes fattened them up and then sold them as slaves to the Mexicans further south.

Never were the Shoshonis a particularly warlike tribe, unlike the Blackfeet who had a reputation for ruthless violence. About 1500 the Shoshonis made their way across the Rockies and began to thrive there as never before. Food

was more abundant and protection more possible in the
mountain canyons. In the early 1700s the Shoshonis began
to acquire horses from their kinsmen, the Commanches.
They seemed to have exceptional skills in breeding, training,
and trading horses. From that time on they were a power to
be reckoned with on the northern plains. One needs to
understand this in relative terms, however. The combined
populations of all the adjoining tribes of the Uto-Aztecan
language group—the Shoshonis, Utes, Piutes, and
Bannocks—probably never exceeded 15,000. The large
expanses they inhabited could easily support such small
numbers.

The first white men the Shoshonis ever saw were those
in the Lewis and Clark expedition of 1805. Sacajawea led
the expedition, a Shoshoni girl who had been captured by
the Hidatsas and sold to the French trapper Charbonneau for
a wife at Fort Mandan where Lewis and Clark spent the
winter. The very first Shoshoni village the expedition came
upon, about four hundred souls, contained many of Sacajawea's people, including her brother, the chief Cameahwait.

Despite, or perhaps because of the vicissitudes of her
fortunes, Sacajawea became something of a cosmopolitan
among Indians. She went all the way to the Pacific with
Lewis and Clark, her infant son strapped to her back. Later
she left Charbonneau, who was nowhere near her equal
either in intelligence or fortitude, and spent a good many
years among the Commanches. When her Commanche
husband died, she again went north and joined her Shoshoni
people on the Wind River. She is reported to have spoken,
an old woman, at the Great Treaty Council at Fort Bridger
in 1868.

Cameahwait, her brother, supplied horses for the Lewis
and Clark expedition so that they were able to make it
across the mountains. His own tribe's political fortunes had
recently fallen on hard times. Although the Shoshonis had
horses and were thus able to hunt buffalo, they were not
supplied with guns as were the more southerly tribes who
came in contact with the Spaniards in Santa Fe. Thus they
were powerless before their enemies' raiding parties. They
had in fact just suffered such a raid from the Blackfeet when
Lewis and Clark appeared. The explorers, whose mission
from the U.S. government was, in part, to effect peace

among the constantly warring tribes, promised Cameahwait that his people would be supplied with adequate defenses against their enemies.

From that time on, the Shoshonis have had a more benign relationship with the white invaders than perhaps any other Indian tribe. By the middle of the nineteenth century, Washakie, their great and crafty chief, had arisen among them, himself a product of one of those raid alliances. His mother was a Shoshoni and his father a Flathead who was killed by the Blackfeet when Washakie was five. Washakie lived among both the Lemhi and the Bannocks before finally settling with the Shoshonis who made him chief after he led a successful raid on the Blackfeet. Perhaps by then Washakie had circulated among the different tribes enough to acknowledge the inevitable. The era of the fur traders and mountain men, whites who survived by assimilating Indian ways, was ending. The Oregon Trail with its unrelenting stream of immigrants was destroying the isolation of the Indians. Their way of life was dying fast. Washakie formed a loose alliance with the government agents and secured for his people one of the best allotments of reservation land in the West. They were never victims of slaughter the way the Arapaho and Cheyenne were at the Sand Creek massacre in Colorado. They were protected from other Indian tribes by white forces. In practically every treaty or agreement with the U.S. government, Washakie secured the Shoshoni advantage.

The days of Washakie and Cameahwait and Sacajawea are over, however. The tribe has a certain amount of income from its reservation oil leases. It gets special federal funds for its schools and public health clinics. Its affairs are run by a tribally elected administrative council, some of whose members no longer even live on the Wind River Reservation. The most recently elected member is an architect who spends a good deal of his time in foreign countries. They all wear polyester rather than buckskin, eat hamburgers instead of pemmican.

This is how a way of life dies. The reservation is only a way station in the death process. Everyone there is in Intensive Care but not expected to live. A certain number of artifacts will survive: the peculiar floral pattern of the Shoshoni beadwork, the hide paintings, perhaps even the style of horsemanship. After all, we still have Celtic crosses and Egyptian amulets. But the Shoshonis no longer live by digging roots, picking berries, or even trading horses. Their link to the land grows more tenuous with every generation.

Their native religion, irritatingly undogmatic to the Western mind, adapts itself easily to other influences. The Sun Dance, its central expression, was itself borrowed from the Algonquin plains tribes in the eighteenth century. The ceremony of fasting, prayer, and ecstatic dancing lasts eight days and has been subtly modified by Christian symbols just as the pagan spring rites of the ancient world were adapted to become a celebration of the Resurrection.

What is particularly painful about the death of a culture is that it takes several generations. An individual, through education and dislocations, may make a leap over several centuries and into another culture, but a group cannot. Cultural death is not quick and clean, like excising a tumor. As with the erosion of mountains, a good deal of rubble goes with it. The wasting of mountains and the wasting of cultures are more analogous to one another than they are to the death of any single small organism.

Ash Wednesday

Dumitru Staniloae, a Romanian theologian, reminds us that the whole world is marked with the cross. Its imprint is not optional, a sign to be chosen only by Christians. No one avoids the cross. Even the most determined hedonist knows his pleasures to be passing away. All people lose what they love in the end, however careful they are to keep it. The cross is not just a symbol for the religious. You do not escape it by becoming secular, by ignoring it, or even by denying it. The cross is the unavoidable stake driven into the heart of all creation. Everything we love, all our desires—our kin, country, laughter, food, songs, spring, galaxies, even our own flesh and our own minds—we lose them all. The very enjoyment of them is always tempered, always damped by this knowledge of eventual loss. It is not only the Christian who anticipates the crucifixion of the world. Unbelievers too know that all their joys will die.

Even a modern pagan like D. H. Lawrence had a firm sense of the necessity of death.

Are you willing to be sponged out, erased, cancelled,
made nothing?
Are you willing to be made nothing?
dipped into oblivion?

If not, you will never really change.

His poem "Phoenix" could in fact serve as an apt meditation
before baptism.

This cross that happens to us all, whether we will or
no, is not a private little affair, a crucifixion of the interior
only. For we bring down with us to death the whole
sensible world, all of creation. Or as Maximus the Confessor
put it, "all the realities which we perceive with the senses
demand the cross" and "all realities which we understand
with our mind have need of the tomb." It is not only we
who must die to be transformed, but the entire cosmos. We
cannot extricate ourselves, even in death, from creation. Its
destiny depends on ours. Only if we make a good job of
dying will creation have a chance for redemption.

How much of my tenuous and half-hearted life has been
spent in protecting myself, a self I could in reality no more
shield from the forces hostile to it than hold back the
avalanche that took out the side of Arrow Mountain?

Home, family, learning, places, skill, experience—this is
the world I have, quite literally, spent my life gaining. And
gaining, I find upon reflection, is not in itself wicked.
Rather, quite the reverse. It is only wicked when it is self-
contained, dammed up in itself. All gain must in fact be
given up, turned over, spent. It is only in the giving up that
the gain achieves reality. Otherwise, hoarded, it immediately
begins to decline from its reality, slip from its potential and
potency into festering and suppuration. Home must be spent
on hospitality; children given up in marriage; skill offered in
work that acquires a life of its own. Not a shred of what we
call life, not a bare bone, are we ever left to gnaw alone in
a sullen, solitary corner.

Some saint once said he always tried to get rid of
money as quickly as he could, before it corrupted him. So
should we spend all our lives, quickly, fluidly. All our assets
should be liquid so they can run easily through our fingers.
Try to keep one bit back and it turns stagnant and stinking.
Thus eternity depends on transience, as life depends on the

cross. Only as the world is crucified to us and we to the world is creation able to live.

In Orthodox liturgy, Staniloae reminds us, the eucharistic loaf, the sign of God's gift and man's work, has pressed into it the mark of the cross. "With this sign the priest blesses the water of Baptism, and also the holy water with which he sprinkles the house, the fields and the whole world in which the Christian lives and works—all is covered with the sign of the cross."

Everything we have, everything we are, belongs to death. Whatever other fortunes befall us during our transitory existence, this waits for us all. We really have only two choices: doomed defiance, including the defiance of despair, or taking up the cross.

Why are we asked for this one thing, which is everything—our life? Why is the whole world poised upon the point of that paradox at the center of all existence? And the paradox is not just at the center of our mental existence or abstracted thought, but at the center of atoms, metabolism, even light itself. Why is it such an *objective* reality that, as T. S. Eliot wrote, "our only health is the disease"? Why can't it only be a figure of speech? Why aren't the purgatorial fires, "of which the flame is roses, and the smoke is briars," only metaphorical? Why is death *real?* And not only real but necessary?

The drama demands it. If we weren't asked for the absolutely hardest thing possible, but only, say, the second or third, then aesthetically the whole structure of the story would be flawed. History would be a failure. The world he created as a gift, the people upon whom he had set his own image and likeness were all catastrophically marred. What else could accomplish the denouement necessary to that story except the giving back of everything, the return of creation, including our own lives? How else indeed are all things to be restored? Does not our grasp upon the little broken bits of our lives in fact stand in the way of the redemption of all creation? Taking up the cross is not something we do to save our own precious little souls. It is an action taken on behalf of the whole cosmos. Unbelievers do not simply damn themselves; they damn the world. The early church fathers said that whoever is nourished by the cross is nourished by the tree of life.

But learning to love the cross is a lifelong undertaking. I am such a half-hearted cross-bearer. I pick it up and drag it a few feet, only to drop it and go wandering off in the direction of the first distraction that offers itself.

Still, I love it best during Lent. It is good to have a season for the cross so that one can concentrate. In the dead of winter, the cross appears such a feasible reality. No flowers, no birds, no sign of life distracts me from this death. With so few enticements to life, one can, as Staniloae describes it, remain in one's sorrow, "carrying his cross, without taking refuge in a new pleasure."

Today David shaved off the beard he had worn for fifteen years, two-thirds of our lives together. For some reason, quite suddenly, the idea occurred to us both simultaneously. I was curious to see what changes his countenance had undergone during those years. So was he.

Neither one of us recognized him. It was as though he was gone and a stranger had suddenly stepped into his skin. Yet not a complete stranger. I recognized the boy I had married many years ago.

A hidden self has suddenly been disinterred. The mouth, particularly, is so quick to respond, a feature obscured by the beard. The eyes, of course, are the same. I recognize them even though their total effect is altered by the change in the rest of the face. Altogether, it is a face of great vulnerability and sweetness. It has lain all these years like the seed hidden in the earth.

We are living in a Lenten landscape. All our senses are fasting. Edwin Way Teale, a writer who belongs to that lost category of "naturalist," has pointed out that the world is in fact not so dead as it appears. "Within the earth there are roots and seeds; on the bare twigs, there are winter buds; buried in the soil and mud beneath ice-locked water are the turtles and frogs and dragonfly nymphs; hidden in decaying logs and under snow-covered debris are the fertilized queens of wasps and bumblebees. Everywhere, on all sides of us, as far as winter reigns, life is suspended temporarily."

That is no doubt true. Still, life is not accessible to our senses. It has removed itself to a realm outside our reach. It may be there, waiting for the proper moment to reappear,

but it is distant from us now. This is the time of fasting, of
sensory deprivation, when the Bridegroom has gone away.
We feel malnourished, sense the scurvy clouding our vision,
our legs growing rickety.

All we've got is a little more light. Almost two hours
more a day now than in the dead of winter. It is not quite
dark yet when we eat our supper. We can still make out the
outline of the mountains then. But the extra light only
reveals more of our poverty, leaves our perceptions starving
longer every day.

I walk up a path this morning that I had occasion to
walk down yesterday afternoon when the temperature had
risen above freezing. I left my boot tracks in the solvent
mud then, as deep as an inch in places. This morning those
tracks are frozen solid, looking like a series of receding
plaster casts. Perhaps by midday they will begin to melt
again; the water, released from its crystals, will run from
between the solid grains of grit, washing some of them
downward too. Gradually, over a period of days, the tracks
will blur and then disappear.

With these few hours of thawing each day, the earth
twitches its skin. Rocks sprout, confounding us in the road.
They are heaved out by the expansion and contraction of the
ground on the slopes. The earth moves a lot more than one
might suspect. And by this shuffling, this twitching, the
ground tenderizes itself, makes minuscule pockets of air,
places where water can seep and carry down with it the
seemingly inconsequential bits of organic matter that
eventually, over thousands of years, will become a layer of
soil.

Gradations of time, small increments of change, are
essential to life. Butterfly larvae, Teale tells us, "can be
frozen so hard they shatter like glass on the floor. Yet, if
they are thawed out very slowly, they show no ill effects."
They can, in fact, be refrozen and thawed any number of
times and in the end still come to their winged completion
despite their repeated descent into death. "The trick lies in
the gradual change. Frogs have shown that they can stand
water that is so hot it burns the skin, if the fluid is heated
slowly enough."

Here we are, like frozen butterfly larvae, being careful

not to bang our crystalline hearts against the stony surfaces that surround us lest they shatter into needlelike shards. No doubt, if we were suddenly propelled from the dead center of winter into the wild jubilation of spring, that impact would explode us into splinters.

But the thawing has, in fact, begun. Right now it is mostly a matter of more light. The earth warms slowly from its sleep. At night one hears the predators howling with hunger. The land-based economy in the canyon is getting very low, despite the light. The owls and the coyotes start a chorus as the moon rises in the evening. Hoots and howls from hunger. Their supply of small rodents is getting sparse. The coyotes are coming in closer to human habitats that the mice and rabbits have counted on for protection till now. A friend who lives further up the canyon close to the trailhead has already lost a big yellow cat to the coyotes. She is worried about her other cat and her dog, a Chesapeake retriever as large as a coyote itself. Once the coyotes make a kill, our friend says, they hang around the same place, hoping for more. Even the dog could not stand up to a determined pair of coyotes.

It will take time, time for the soil to warm, the moisture to flow, the grass to green, so that the gophers and ground squirrels will wake up and stumble out of their burrows, the rabbits and mice get their first mouthfuls of fresh fodder, before the coyotes themselves can get a decent meal.

Another letter from yet another friend about a marriage that, if not dead, is certainly in the frozen state of rockhard butterfly larvae. And last week there was another such letter, except in that case the larva had already dropped and shattered. As long as the postal service still works, it seems, there is no escape from this kind of knowledge. We may barricade ourselves here in the mountains, tune our guitar and mandolin, sing, fish in fair weather, build up our woodpile, watch the beaver, the sheep, and the deer, take the census of birds, but still the traces of that thing we call human society will seep through, like paratyphoid from a neighboring horse tank.

It only happens in words. On one level, these are mere streaks of carbon on a sheet of white paper. If I took the envelopes out unopened and laid them among the rocks, they would only become tatters of litter there. The petroglyphs on the cliff walls would mean more immediately than these abstracted curves and hollows and stilts we call words. It is my own misfortune that I can read. Because I can take these marks, each one made by the inconsequential pressure of a fingertip on a typewriter key, and shift them around into the outlines of faces and places, filling in the outlines with my own store of memoried color and light and motion—because I have learned this trick, I am now a hollow well down which other people throw their pain, listening for the echo as it hits the bottom. That's what you get for learning how to read. They never taught us that with *Dick and Jane,* who, you will remember, lived on Pleasant Street.

Well, it's too late now. Once you receive word that the world is coming unwedded and unwelded, you can't go back and unknow it. I hold the letters as if they were a sheaf of lab reports that inform me of the extent of the disease. It won't do any good now to go out and scatter the slips of paper among the stones, turning them to litter instead of letters. The parcels of pain are already ringing against the rounded walls of the well.

Actually, I have a theory about pain. It came to me while reading about the clipping Annie Dillard keeps stuck in her mirror. The one with the bandaged face of the man who had been burned twice and was convinced God hated him. The burnt man seemed to be filled to overflowing, both physically and every other way, with pain. One is awed, humbled, or at least made nervous by his experience. My theory, however, is this: pain expands to fill the space available. This man, I don't suppose, could hold any more without dying or going crazy. But my friend who wrote the letter, who licked the stamp and sealed the envelope, who is not swathed in bandages or shuddering from exposed nerve-endings, nevertheless tells me she can barely stand to live. She is as close to suicide as the seared man.

This intrigues me. One looks at pictures of the Sahel refugees. The children look like corpses already bloating from death. Grief that has receded beyond emotion is engraved on the faces of these people. Seeing such suffering, one hopes never to have to look at a yellow smiley-face again. The question is, how can anyone, having witnessed humans suffering *in extremis,* at the utter limits just before the point at which consciousness must succumb in blessed oblivion, how can any of the rest of us claim pain? A death in the family: what is that to the extinction of all one's earthly ties, one by one and before one's helpless eyes? A betrayal by one beloved: what is that to the betrayal by God?

The only answer seems to be that the economy of pain is not as inorganic as the exchange of, say, metal currency. George Bernard Shaw said that if you "die of starvation, you will suffer all the starvation there has been or will be. If ten thousand people die with you, their participation in your lot will not make you be ten thousand times more hungry nor multiply the time of your agony ten thousand times. Do not let yourself be overcome by the horrible sum of human sufferings; such a sum does not exist." And C. S. Lewis obviously agreed with him. "Suppose that I have a toothache of intensity x: and suppose that you, who are seated beside me, also begin to have a toothache of intensity x. You may, if you choose, say that the total amount of pain in the room is now $2x$. But you must remember that no one is suffering $2x$: search all time and all space and you will not find that composite pain in anyone's consciousness."

One cannot measure pain by weight, volume, or density. A fly in the ointment can weigh as heavy as all the heaped up corpses of the starved Sahelese. I know it seems an obscene equation, but that is how the human psyche works. The refusal of a certain tongue to articulate the words "I love you" can make life as bleak as the desert, as tormenting as the burn-bed. It is no good pointing out to people in pain that things could be worse. The pain, whatever its source, is already filling every nook and cranny of their consciousness, all the space available. You can supply new sources of pain, put them on the rack, confiscate their property, sell them into slavery, make a Job of them, but all you do is divert them from one pain to another.

The burned man is a terrifying case. Whether his is more or less terrifying than the Sahel refugees I have no means of measuring. And my friends whose lives are broken open like aborted butterfly larvae but who are not starving or watching their children starve, who have not had their hide charred off twice, do I say their pain has not yet reached its proper pitch? That they have no business moaning in their bourgeois agony? Not, surely, if their misfortune is sufficient to make life hateful to them. Any time someone wants to die, even a jilted teenager, I suppose you've got to take it seriously.

Saint Ignatius of Antioch wanted to die, but not because he hated life. He was arrested by Roman civil officials during the second-century reign of the Emperor Trajan as an "atheist," meaning he refused to renounce Christ and acknowledge the deity of the Emperor. The terms of the refusal were quite clear: death by public spectacle in the arena at Rome, the fashion at the time being rending by wild beasts. No doubt it took a fair amount of courage for Ignatius to make up his mind. His temperament, one gathers from his letters, was not fiery and impetuous like that of Paul, by whom he had probably been converted. He seems a gentle enough soul, almost apologetic about his coming martyrdom. Apologetic but nevertheless tenacious. He sent letters ahead of him to the church at Rome, begging them to renounce their plans to intercede for him with the pagan authorities. "I am afraid of your love," he writes,

> it may do me wrong. It is easy for you to have your way, but, if you do not yield to me, it will be hard for me to reach God. . . . If only you will say nothing on my behalf, I shall be a word of God. But, if your love is for my body, I shall be once more a mere voice. . . . I beseech you not to indulge your benevolence at the wrong time. Please let me be thrown to the wild beasts; through them I can reach God. I am God's wheat; I am ground by the teeth of the wild beasts that I may end as the pure bread of Christ. Pardon me, but I know what is good for me. I am now beginning to be a disciple; may nothing visible or invisible prevent me from reaching Jesus Christ. . . . My search is for him who died for us. The pangs of the new birth are upon me. Forgive me, brethren. Do not prevent this new life. . . . When I reach it, I shall be fully a man.

Ignatius wrote this letter during a wave of persecution when the church was forced to establish a policy on martyrdom. Some zealots, it seems, were showing up at the Colosseum door, demanding to be thrown to the lions posthaste. Unfortunately, their zeal at the *idea* of martyrdom cooled considerably when they were presented with the actual lions. The high resolve of the the would-be martyrs evaporated, and they found themselves suddenly on their knees, renouncing Christ and doing obeisance to the emperor. To spare everyone these embarrassing scenes, the church taught that no one was to actively seek martyrdom. If actually arrested by the authorities, Christians were to stand firm and persevere in their confession of Christ. Otherwise, they were to mind their own business.

Ignatius, of course, had not thrown himself into the arms of the authorities. As the bishop of Antioch he was being made an example in order to undermine the faith of the cowardly and also to weaken the church by taking away its leader. Still, he is pushing the limits of the church's policy. Here is a man so hungry for God he is eager to be eaten in order to taste him. Ignatius did not falter in the arena. He had his way. He embraced death, embraced the beasts. He was that hungry for God.

Most of us try to keep the wild beasts chained up in the backyard. Since pain has a contrary nature and battens on neglect, we try to feed it only as much of ourselves as will keep it barely under control, give it only enough of our attention to keep it from growing monstrous and taking over the neighborhood. This is called good mental health. A few, whose mental health is obviously questionable, try to cozy up to the beast, to see things from its point of view. They are like the overconfident volunteers for martyrdom. We call them masochists today. But an even fewer number, who know full well the danger and the implacable hostility they face, nevertheless unchain the beast and take him on. They know from the beginning there is no question of vanquishing him, except as his open jaws become the yawning gate of the birth canal into light.

Our age hasn't much talent for martyrdom. For one thing, we are thwarted by benign and unobliging authorities. The wild beasts are kept in the zoo, not the arena today. We have had to satisfy ourselves with less abrupt ways to God. We like to describe these ways as pilgrimages, though our knowledge of such a metaphor is almost exclusively literary. What we have in mind is actually a guided tour. Whereas it used to take savage beasts in the Colosseum to fill our pain quotient to capacity, now it takes only a spouse treading on the toes of our self-esteem.

I do not disparage or discount that pain. In any case, it's about all Western bourgeois Christians have got to work with. It may be lacking in drama and mythic depth, but it's the vehicle supplied by our culture and time. And as Bunyan, who still lived in the age of actual pilgrimages, said: "Some also have wished that the next way to their father's house were here, and that they might be troubled no more with either mountains or hills to get over, but the way is the way, and there is an end."

We hiked up to Lake Louise today. We went because of the unseasonably warm February day. It was well above freezing on the canyon floor. Sun but no wind. A rare combination in Wyoming. There were no signs of spring approaching on the trail, however, despite the mud and melting snow on its lower end. But as we stretched out to eat our lunch on a boulder field halfway up the trail, the light was so bodied and palpable we could have fed on it and felt our eyes growing fat. Lush light, swelling with strength.

The trail to Lake Louise climbs only a thousand feet as it makes its way three crow-flight miles closer to the continental divide. That difference in altitude provides, however, a stark contrast. Winter is a long way from over here, however it may thaw at the cabin. Nothing has melted at the upper end of the trail. All the moisture is still solid, locked up in ice. Lake Louise itself is covered with snow drifts as deep as dunes. They are honed to a knife edge by the wind that whistles, compressed, through the high walls of the mountain col.

We walk out onto the frozen lake, explore its far end that in summer is inaccessible because of the steep cliffs that wall it in. Glaciers loom over us. A cascade of green ice hundreds of feet high hangs suspended from the cliff's stone face. The ice is pure here; it is not mottled like the lower falls, because here nothing melts and nothing moves all winter. The trees on the cliff sides are black and blasted, some by an old fire, some by the constant wind. Is this what the inside of a martyr's soul looks like, austere, implacable? We hold hands and creep around the edges of the ice, hoping to avoid its notice, feeling as though we have stumbled into a scene too exalted for our frailties.

I recall a sign I saw once at a ranger station high in the Colorado Rockies at the outset of a cross-country ski trail. At the bottom of its list of hazards likely to be encountered on the trail was one final bleak admonition: "Remember. The mountains don't care."

Second Sunday in Lent

The vicar looks particularly parboiled today, like a lobster that has just this moment been plunged into boiling water and is still suffering the agony that comes right before the nerve cells explode and feel no more.

I know what he is going to say in the space right after the processional hymn, even before he says it. I've known it in fact for two days now, ever since his wife brought her red eyes and freckles and shapeless cardigan into our cabin ten miles out in the wilderness. She had her speech made out ahead of time; like Polycarp as he leapt into the fire, she said it all in a rush to get it over with, handing us in one single motion the whole thing in a nutshell.

"Okay," we say, fingering the nutshell gingerly. We'd recognize it anywhere, even when it doesn't come in envelopes. "I see. So. Your beast in the backyard has gotten loose. Well. Hold that tiger."

I am pleased, really pleased, that she has come to tell us good-by before she leaves. Pleased that she has brought along the beast latched to her throat to let it have a nip at us too. A nip is all it gets though. It is, after all, her beast, not mine. She can only share her grief, not abdicate it, not give it away like a cold.

And now the priest is standing in front of the congregation in this little church no bigger than Noah's ark and occasionally glancing down at a piece of paper where he has put words down like stones in a stream to get him across to the other side, to get through this that somehow must be gotten through. *This way*, as Bunyan said, *that is the way, and there's an end.*

Meanwhile his beast, a black jaguar, roams up and down the aisles, silently savaging the members of Christ's body. Some of them see the jaguar coming and shrink from the assault. Others are caught off guard as it crouches in the shadows, the jewel light from the windows speckling its coat; they do not notice it until it springs upon them, snarling. There are those around me who, I can tell from their shocked looks, had imagined these pews to be beast-proof, a certain refuge from the mauling that has come upon them so suddenly. As for me, I stare it as straight in the yellow eyes as I can stand, not, certainly, in order to put it out of countenance nor to tame it like a snake, but to mesmerize myself with its reality. I have a theory that if you look at it hard enough, you will to some extent be distracted from the teeth and tearing.

The priest is through now. He has made it to the other side. We go to work on the liturgy, turning the pages with our freshly mangled hands, singing the *Gloria* from punctured lungs. The lay reader gets up and reads the Old Testament lesson about Abraham hacking up his heifer, the goat, and the ram under the oaks at Mamre in order to mark his covenant with God. "Then the birds of prey came down on the carcasses, but Abram drove them away." Today we are all carcasses here in the pews, sacrifices to the vicar's pain.

The epistle and the gospel are read to a massacre. We keep up the singing in a scarecrow's attempt to keep off the vultures. We stick out our bloody stumps to one another, smiling, for the passing of the peace. When the offering plate is passed, we drip into it.

Finally, we stagger as far as the Eucharist. Like the walking wounded, we line up in the aisle, courteously averting our eyes from the gashed faces of our neighbors. The jaguar has indeed done a creditable number on this flock of heifers, goats, and rams. It sits, almost docile now, and licks its paws fastidiously at the feet of its owner. As always after inflicting its wounds, it has grown visibly smaller, at least for the moment.

We get to the communion rail on our knees, crawling. With his own boiled and peeled fingers, the priest presses the wafer into the wounds we hold up. The chalice bearer pours the antiseptic down our throats. There. We stand up. We feel better already. We take deep breaths and look around. Everybody seems in fine fettle. We grin at one another like still giddy convalescents.

We limp into the light outside, bandaged with the wafers, our wounds stinging but clean from their washing in wine.

We have stood still and submitted to another's pain. And we are well, healed by yet another's still flowing wounds. The whole world is awash in redemption.

Tonight there is a full moon. I watch it come up over the eastern ridge, a huge, thin silver wafer. The coyotes howl at it all night as it arches across the sky.

March

The lakes are beginning to resemble the surface of the moon. Patches of snow lie whitely across the blued ice, marbling its skin, just as the moon's mountains make it look mottled from earth. Torrey, Ring, and Trail all lie like flattened pieces of moon that have fallen to earth between these canyon walls. It will take a while for the two feet of ice to melt, but soon the lakes will be coming apart.

News of more illness in my family. My grandfather's heart has begun to trip over itself. He has only just completed his last house at eighty-five, built on the same pattern that has always seemed sensible to him: a rectangle divided down its middle both ways into four rooms. He had been clearing brush for a watermelon patch and rose bushes.

Our elder daughter calls with the news she has broken her leg skiing and is getting married in June.

In town, a friend, older than I am, is ready any day now to go to the hospital in Riverton to have her baby.

Life is too fast. I can't keep up with it. Something is always either coming together or breaking apart. The pace is too much for me. I'll go and sit beside a slow stone while the lichens dissolve its skin with acid at a speed I can stand.

March 4, my birthday

I was a winter baby, a fact that accounts perhaps for my predisposition to starkness, austerity, and Calvinism. I like to start with the worst possible case and work from there. Was this because the first world I knew was winter? They tell me it was a dreary, rain-soaked morning when they took my mother to the hospital in Houston.

Today it is sunny in Wyoming. Torrents are washing away the coast of California; there is snow south of us, and ice storms in the Dakotas, but here the sun is shining and one can walk around outside in a light coat. I am not starting this year at any rate with the worst possible case.

It is embarrassing to admit it, but my birthday is one of the two most exciting days of the year for me. Age is irrelevant at this point. For years now I have felt the same age I was at my baptism: eight. There was a period in my late twenties and early thirties when I got as old as I ever expect to. But now I feel the same age all the time.

This is not to deny that I am progressing toward death. I can see quite plainly in the mirror that my flesh is sinking, like any avalanche descending a slope. Gravity pulls at it, gaining more ground every year. The skin, once so elastic and mobile, freezes into the folds and wrinkles of our most characteristic expressions. We become living monuments to ourselves, not unlike Lot's wife. In our joints, the giant molecules rivet themselves like bridge spans; we turn into living erector sets. Our joints stiffen and freeze. We can no longer stand up straight, touch our toes, play the piano, write a legible hand. There is no more warm, gentle sluicing of body fluids through the spongy, slushy internal organs. All those tubes and hoses, down to the smallest molecular pump in the mitochondria, begin to petrify like old, cracked radiator hoses on an automobile.

In fact, the chemical process is the same in radiators and livers: molecular cross-linking. It is the same process that turns raw hide into leather. Apply tannin to animal skin and it reacts with the protein molecules to form a series of rigid struts. As they lock consecutively and securely into place, the hide hardens into leather. The same process happens inside us as we age. Instead of the rhythmic internal tides that carried the blood cells along so swimmingly, a sluggish flux creeps through the maze of inflexible, leathery tunnels. We are turning to a pillar of salt.

It's all downhill from here on, at least so far as the body is concerned. We may slalom back and forth across the face of the hill, using the switchbacks judiciously to slow our descent. But a descent it inevitably is, no matter how gradual. Despite health foods and vitamins, despite exercises and biofeedback, the trend, though barely perceptible, is relentlessly downward. We begin to look like candle stubs. The victory of gravity begins to show in the folds of flesh that hang about us like dripping wax. Cheeks become jowls; pouches beneath the eyes slide earthward in the slow avalanche of years. A dewlap develops on the once columnar throat. Breasts hang like shriveling gourds. Everything is sagging earthward as though in answer to a prophetic geotropism, as though the body recognizes where it is headed. And like the candle stub, we actually grow shorter with age, shrinking and shriveling as we burn up, whether at both ends or only one.

Indeed, burning up is precisely what we're doing. Paper that turns yellow with age is actually doing a slow burn. The carbon and hydrogen it is made of are combining with the oxygen in the air, only gradually, instead of quickly in a blaze. Iron rusting is the same process of slow oxidation. We speak, accurately, of burning up energy, of oxidizing food in our bodies. Bodies are often compared to automobiles or furnaces for this reason: there is a fire hidden inside that powers them. But neither cars nor furnaces nor bodies go on burning forever. Eventually the very process that has provided their power and for which they have been the container begins to eat at their own innards. The sleek sides of the pistons are clogged with the debris of combustion. The guts of the furnace are infinitesimally consumed along with the fuel. And our bodies too smolder in slow self-immolation.

Oxidation is also, of course, the process by which we live. The inhaled oxygen molecules combine with the fuel we stoke ourselves with to produce energy and movement, to grow and repair the body. But oxidation is also what we die from. The oxygen molecule, one of the simplest constructions in the cosmos, indeed among the most abundant of the elements on earth, is the agent of both life and death. The Lord giveth and the Lord taketh away—and he does it most often through oxygen.

Oxygen atoms themselves get knocked around a good bit in the atmosphere. They may get a few electrons knocked off by lightning or too much radiation from the sun. These scruffy oxygen molecules are called "free radicals." Electrons askew, these free radicals, after being breathed in, amble through the bloodstream like gangs of hooligans looking for trouble. Instead of combining with the food we've eaten to produce energy, they tend to seep through cell walls and vandalize the contents, interfering with enzymes, ripping apart the message system of genetic strands. When the code for new cells is passed on, the information is so distorted by these free radicals that it causes either the death or mutation of the new cells. Under such attacks, collagen, the glue that sticks one cell to another, and elastin, the protein of elastic tissue, collapses. Free radicals also catch up whatever

polyunsaturated fat molecules they can and form a kind of
vitrified ash that clogs the cell and eventually weighs down
the tissues and organs of the body. No wonder we begin to
sag. We're becoming a veritable garbage bag, a slag heap, a
walking compost pile, a burnt-out case.

As if this weren't enough, there occurs at some point in
the aging process a kind of cellular insanity, a sort of
protoplasmic senility. It has its origin just beneath the
breastbone in a small gland called the thymus. There,
throughout all our youthful uphill years and for a good
number of the downside ones, this scrap of tissue produces
a type of white blood cell known as the T-cell. These are
the militia of the bloodstream, coded to seek out any foreign
invader not marked with the body's peculiar password, a
chemical design stamped on each cell's surface. Any such
invader they instantly surround. Anything from a browsing
bacterium to a transplanted kidney can set off the T-cells'
alarm system and call up a horde of frenzied antibodies. In
this way the body protects itself from disease. The T-cells
memorize the strange chemical code marked on the
membrane of each invader and order up antibodies
specifically designed to attack that particular enemy. With
those antibodies stored in its arsenal, the body becomes
immune to that particular disease.

At a certain point, however, something seems to go
wrong. The T-cells, like paranoid old soldiers, begin to see
enemies everywhere, under every bed and behind every
bush. Some strange mutation takes place in their translation
of the body's password. They start attacking their own
perfectly normal cells. They no longer distinguish between
friend and foe. The trained commando squads of T-cells turn
into terrorists, irrational and uncontrollable. Civil war smokes
in the blood stream. The body becomes autoimmune.

Sometimes the body becomes immune to itself well
before old age. Then we call the results of such internal
warfare a disease. Certain kinds of arthritis, lupus, hepatitis,
some anemia, even certain infantile skin diseases are results
of this cellular paranoia, this inability to distinguish self
from nonself. In aging the process works more slowly. The
T-cells grow tired and do not operate as effectively or
accurately as before. Only gradually does senescence set in.

Still, however slowly age creeps upon us, the outcome is

inevitable. The body, no matter how well cared for, no matter how diligently bolstered and propped, either by modern science or ancient disciplines, wears out. A genetic clock rings somewhere in those distant internal caverns, informing the cells their time is up.

Gradually, we begin to replace our necessary parts. Spectacles, false teeth, a hearing aid, a heart valve. The rest we simply patch up as best we can. A plastic surgeon may cut out slivers of sagging flesh and stitch the edges back together tighter. *There. That'll hold you a few more years.* Organs begin to fall away like dried and withered petals at the blossom end of the fruit. *Here. You won't need those ovaries any more. One kidney should do. We'll simply resection the stomach here ...*

What's happening? That's *you* being discarded so casually. That flaccid piece of muscle clipped neatly from its supporting struts and sent to the lab for sectioning and then for disposal in the incinerator, that's the haven that held and expelled three children into this world. Even if it never contracts another time, even if it ceases to function, it at least has the status of an artifact. It's you. Well, that part of you is gone now.

A network of fine lines appears on the face, neck, hands, arms. Indeed they are so fine as to be fascinating in themselves. The tracery, minute and delicate, has its own sort of beauty. Not the firm fullness of youth, certainly, but an etching of acid, intricacy of line instead of the broad strokes of rising color. Every year there will be more lines, not less. There is no reversing the process. The elastin stretches itself to its limit and then gives way altogether. We develop the same pale lackluster skin we remember in our parents, the same purple, vermiform veins behind the knees and on the thighs. We become what we, in our youth, found so repellant—a betrayed body.

And why do we have to spend at least half our lifetime on the downward side of the hill? Why a hill at all? Why not a cliff, from which we launch out directly from the summit of our physical perfection?

Methuselah, Noah's grandfather, lived to be 969 years old. When did he start downhill? Not till after he was 187 anyway, when he begat Lamech his first child. It seems that if one lives such a long stretch, he also gets off to a correspondingly slow start. Did several centuries of decline overshadow two hundred years of youth? Long life was held in esteem by the Israelites. The reward for honoring one's parents was length of days. Abraham, we are told, lived to "a good old age, an old man, and full of years." One hundred and seventy-five, in fact. David's end, however, was not so pleasant. The young poet-warrior, full of vigorous juices, lusting for conquest, women, and sacred songs, had obviously oxidated at a terrific rate. When he was "old and stricken in years" the servants swaddled him in bedclothes, but to no avail: "he gat no heat." The common lot, even of kings who have burnt the candle at both ends. The young Shunammite maiden, Abishag, was given the somewhat dubious honor of warming his withered, hypothermic body a while longer. Despite her efforts, David's lifespan in no way equaled his distant antediluvian ancestors who seem to have oxidated so much slower.

There is yet another curious aspect of aging. Every day people pray to be cured of everything from cancer to colic. No malady strikes us as being outside the bounds of heavenly help. One may ask for and expect supernatural aid in healing diseases. But aging—who has petitioned to be spared the slow, and seemingly natural disintegration of the body? Who is so impudent as to ask for protection from the assault of wrinkles and gray hair?

Not only is an unseemly resistance to aging ludicrous, it strikes us as monstrous even, the idea of the body that refuses to age. In science fiction and fairy tales an old consciousness encased in a deceptively youthful exterior bodes nobody well. Snow White's stepmother horrifies us most because she is an old hag disguised as a young beauty. We find repugnant those people whose outsides promise more than their insides deliver. Bodies that are not marked by their passing years disgust us. We feel the wear and tear ought to show somehow. Our experience must manifest itself in our bodies or else it lacks reality.

It is funny how one gets in the habit of saying, half defensively, half desperately, *I don't look so bad. Not for thirty-five, not for forty.* Certainly rocks are not perturbed by their eroding surfaces nor mountains by the degradation of their slopes.

I am learning to look at myself in the mirror with more

of a mountain's detachment. (What choice do I have, anyway?) The only mirror we've had for six months now has been the little one over the sink where we brush our teeth. I can't even see how I look in the new jacket David has given me for my birthday. Not having mirrors has saved me quantities of time and energy.

My father-in-law used to reckon that life was still acceptable "as long as you've got your health." He did not start with the worst possible case. He clung to a condition. But life allows no conditions. My father-in-law lost his health. He is dead now. He was once a handsome man, tall, with curly hair. In his youth he was a prize-fighter.

How long will I be eight years old? Do I have my own secret conditions, hidden even from myself? Do I implicitly reckon from a tacit point: as long as I've got my—what? Health, husband, family, work, wilderness, books, eyes, mind?

I'm not blind, at least not yet. I can see the kinds of things that life exacts from people. I know that tumors sprout in athletes as well as addicts. I have seen what blood vessels bursting in the brain can do to bright people. I see better women than myself made haggard by pain, their admirable tranquillity destroyed. I may be my baptismal age now, but if I were twisted with rheumatoid arthritis, if my blood corpuscles started eating one another so that weariness was the central fact of life, if some disaster befell my daughters, how old would I be then?

I had a friend once whose daughter, in some darkness beyond anyone's imagining, killed her own baby and then shot herself. Yet this friend was as young as I ever hope to be. It can be done. I may start with the worst possible case, but when I come across such evidence as this, it is only right to report it. The friend is a witness, a martyr in the Greek sense of the word, to the fact that it can be done. But I do not claim that absolute age for myself. I know my limits, sense the underlying conditions I still demand of life. "As long as I've got ..."

I came here to die this winter, and, as it is my birthday and less than three weeks till spring, it is time I looked at the corpse to see how it's getting along with the job.

It's got a daughter getting married in June. We have already and unwittingly spent our last Christmas together

here as one family. And Easter, in another month, will be
our last holy day as a whole. The last. I know the
platitudes. Something new will take its place, and so forth.
So what? It is still the loss of what we were, what we were
for twenty-three years. The loss may be compensated, but it
is nevertheless loss.

Okay. Next.

We will be leaving the mountains. Without quite
knowing how it happened, without seeming to have made a
conscious choice (and how do you expect a corpse to
choose?), I am being picked up like a pawn and deposited
in the flat lowlands a thousand miles south and east of this
clean-picked skeleton I live on now. How is my brain going
to operate in all that fetid humidity? How will my
sensibilities survive the suffocating fecundity? Or a paved
road within a quarter mile of my house? Or people who
watch television instead of the returning waterfowl? Mirrors?
How did I get in this predicament?

The man I came here with will be pulled up by the
roots himself and strewn across the country. Such is the
nature of the new work he is undertaking. Our long,
rounded days of absolutely shaped simplicity will be broken,
shattered into memories. We have been together for all but
a few hours every day for months. Now out of months we
will possibly have only a few days. When so much of
ourselves is stored in each other, how can we not be lost
that way? It was easy enough to put our furniture, our
books, our clothes and dishes into storage and live without
them. But how can we store our selves and live without
them?

This is the way you must live when you're eight years
old. At the mercy of someone else. Trusting the choices
made for you by a Father whose face you've never seen.

Third Sunday in Lent

Today the acolyte finally drops the flag. Down it goes—
clatter, crash—right across the front pew. I am trying
desperately to concentrate on the words of the liturgy, but
instead I am attending to the litany of distractions going on
around me. I can't keep my two pairs of glasses juggled
along with the hymnal and the prayer book. My coat keeps
sliding down the pew back and getting wadded up under

me. I touch the edges of the prayers, and my fingers come off. We're halfway through the creed before I find the place. I try to follow the words of the confession intentionally, balancing along the ledge of its thin spine. My mind, bent on perversity, keeps sliding off. The meaning of everything seems to be evading me, running off in a dozen directions while I snatch and grab at its skirts. I want the world to come together, to provide that satisfying sense of coherence.

About the time another acolyte lays her wafer on the altar rail and runs out in tears of junior-high angst, I give up. Okay. So I don't understand today. It is all beyond me. I cannot make a mandala out of this particular morning. There will be no satisfying click as it all comes together, relieving my inner sense of incoherence. No. Today I have only my need. That is all I will carry to the altar this morning. No understanding. No aesthetic experience. No seeing. Just need.

I hold out my hands. The body is pressed in. I open my mouth. The blood is poured in. That's that. Thus is need easily satisfied, though understanding, sensibilities, even curiosity, must wait.

I came here to die to a life of compromise, a life in which a little bit of faith is traded off for a lot of security. We keep hoping that the compromise will shield us from the reality we fear is there, a reality we know our courage is not equal to.

You must understand. I am a naturally timid creature. Any chances I take are out of ignorance or desperation. At this point, I can only say, a little wildly, that I'd rather be ignorant and desperate if that is the sole way to escape compromise.

I would not, like St. Francis, strip off my clothes in the marketplace. I don't like being cold. And if I embraced the leper, it would be as much from stark curiosity as charity, the curiosity that wants to know the worst possible case.

I don't know—empirically—if the just live by faith or not. I do know—empirically—that the *living* live by faith. Those who depend on other sources for life don't live at all. And what I want, solely, is life itself.

The creek is thawing, and on its upper end above the bridge are a pair of Barrow's goldeneye ducks. Another pair has claimed the open water in Lily Pond. They cruise a few feet in one direction, then turn and sail back again, sticking close together. This is not quite their mating season. The males are not displaying themselves yet. They have only gotten to the point of pairing off and establishing their territory. These females are no pushovers. They're waiting to see the males' beaks turn a comely yellow-orange before they commit themselves. That will take at least another month. Meanwhile they practice their floating foreplay formations.

They have come back a little early because the ice has begun to melt. We walk out on Trail in the afternoon. Its surface is growing slushy, and large puddles of water an inch or more deep reflect the westering sun. Now, in its old age, the ice is showing all the winter's history in its stress marks. Footprints made months ago show up opaquely, as do the tire tracks where trucks have driven out to check ice-fishing holes. Every fissure made by freezing and thawing is still visible. And now as the surface starts to melt, fine webs appear where the water runnels from higher levels. I feel like Gulliver, walking across some enormous Brobdingnagian face, seeing every wrinkle and line magnified into a crevasse.

A muskrat climbs out on a lip of ice at the mouth of the creek and begins shelling tiny freshwater clams with its forepaws. It is intent and methodical, working as quickly as a factory hand with a quota to fill. As soon as it has devoured its haul, it swiftly dives again, is gone for maybe ten seconds, and surfaces on the ice bench to repeat the task. Ordinarily muskrats eat aquatic plants—water lilies, reeds, and the like. But Lent, the last of winter, forces them to feed on these tiny clams. Despite the early thawing, there is not yet enough spring to furnish a green sprig.

Two pair of goldeneyes, a muskrat, and melting. These are our first slow signs of life. These and the disappearance of the sheep. We see only a handful now in the upper meadow at the trailhead, sometimes none at all. They are moving to higher ground as the snow melts, though it will be another two months before the lambing starts. Slow signs, but still—something. And I suppose the insect larvae out there are languorously thawing.

Meanwhile, with a mixture of interest and anxiety, we watch Easter speeding toward us. Locked among ice and rocks in our winter sepulchre, we have gotten used to death. Life seems a little too large for us at present. Suddenly, we're not sure resurrection is what we're after. The return of the goldeneyes we can handle. But the ejection of ourselves from the tomb? Whole currents, floods of faces? The fruits of civilization: paved highways, airports, shopping centers, traffic noises, television, newspapers? It's terrifying. A storm of insistent stimuli.

If we have already become so accustomed to winter, the long dead must be very settled indeed. How is Gabriel ever going to get us all up on Judgment Day? Won't we simply roll over and pull the sod up over our ears? Go blow your horn someplace else, we'll say. After all, it's rest that's promised those who labor and are heavy laden. How can you rest and resurrect?

This is a conundrum we don't consider much nowadays. We're big on life, both before and after death. We don't inquire too closely into other states.

But other ages have considered the matter more closely. The Middle Ages, for example, with its death-soaked imagination, made provision for the slow thawing of human larvae into life. According to their lights, one was not simply ejected from the grave to shatter suddenly on the steps of glory. Purgatory was placed between the darkness of the deathbed and the light inaccessible. Like divers ascending from the depths of high pressure to the upper regions of rarefied air, the dead needed a spiritual decompression chamber so that the heavenly atmosphere wouldn't kill them. Sanctification, even in its terrestrial mode, is a slow process. Who knows how long it might take us to get the toxic gases out of our spiritual blood?

At any rate, the Middle Ages took this problem seriously enough to make Purgatory both a political football and a part of the economy. Pope Gregory X was even willing to concede the doctrine of Purgatory to the Eastern church at the Council of Lyons in 1274. He was, of course, motivated by a desire to unify the eastern and western branches of Christendom against the heathen infidels in the last Crusades. In those days it was Purgatory and prayers for the dead that had potent political effects. Such concerns have been replaced in our day, at least in the West, by the per-gallon price of crude oil. This is civilization as we know it.

The concept of a preparation for beatitude provided the theme and plot for the most important literary enterprise of the Middle Ages. Dante's *Divine Comedy* has as its centerpiece Mount Purgatory. This stony outcropping became such a prominent feature in the age's imaginative geography that it influenced Europe's economic indicators. Even before the Council of Lyons, bequests were made to churches and religious orders providing for continual prayers for the living as well as the dead. But at some point in the thirteenth century the balance of such contributions tipped toward prayers for those in Purgatory. The patrons who funded the construction of the Lady Chapel in Westminster Cathedral, for example, were guaranteed thirteen masses for the living during major church festivals. But they also got for their money twenty masses for the dead every single week of the year. People took Purgatory as seriously and as certainly as they did this life.

Individual priests were paid by wealthy patrons to do nothing but pray and celebrate mass for the family's dead members. Edward I set up perpetual endowments for masses at four different locations for his wife Eleanor of Castile "whom living I have dearly cherished and whom dead I shall not cease to love."

Such chantries clearly helped the unemployment problem among the clergy. And Westminster got no less than twenty-two manorial estates out of the deal with Edward I. Purgatory, in other words, meant profit for the church. That fact in itself is a fairly accurate gauge of how seriously the doctrine was held.

Purgatory had a theological ancestor, however. The notion of some kind of spiritual stopping-off place—a weigh station of the soul on its path to glory—was incorporated into the imagination of the church quite early in Christian history. The precedent to Purgatory was Abraham's bosom, referred to by Christ in the parable of the rich man and Lazarus.

Tertullian, writing his diatribe against Marcion about A.D. 207, says that "there is a spatial concept that may be called Abraham's bosom for receiving the souls of all peoples ... which, though not celestial, is above the lower regions, to

provide refreshment *[refrigerium]* to the souls of the just
until the consummation of all things in the general
resurrection." A couple of centuries later, Augustine wrote of
his dead friend Nebridius going to Abraham's bosom:
"Whatsoever state that be, which is signified by that bosom,
there lives Nebridius my sweet friend . . . for what other
place is there for such a soul?" And Aquinas in the
thirteenth century confirmed this: "That rest which is given
men after death is called the bosom of Abraham."

One sees representations of this *refrigerium* well into
the early Middle Ages. On one of the portals of the
Bamberg cathedral, for instance, is the stone embodiment of
an avuncular Abraham holding several child-sized souls
standing in his lap. They are all, including the patriarch,
grinning from ear to ear. At Moissac, a Romanesque church
illustrates the parable of Lazarus and Dives in stone above
its porch. Abraham, with exceedingly long mandarin
moustaches and a genial smile, cradles in his bosom a child-
sized Lazarus.

Abraham's bosom was obviously more hospitable than
Purgatory. Still, the reduced figures there represent the
remaining immaturity of the recently dead. They illustrate an
implied expectation of growth. Abraham's bosom may be a
rest and a refreshment, but it is not the end of the soul's
story.

Contemporary social critics say that our culture denies
death, but this is not altogether true. For what we deny
with one hand, we affirm with the other. Like death's coy
mistress, we raise one hand, palm outward, in rejection, and
with the other we beckon death seductively. We kill others,
kill ourselves, kill the land, kill the next generation—not
just in a desultory fashion, but with genuine zeal. From our
abortion statistics it sometimes seems we conceive only to
have more scope for killing.

I think we have this problem, this schizophrenia of
devotion and defiance, because in our age's imagination
death is the end. Not just the dark unknown, but the
absolute finale.

The Middle Ages were perhaps the last moment in
history when this was not so. For them, as for all the ages
that went before, death was not the end. Whether the next
stop after this life was Abraham's bosom or Purgatory—or

even Sheol, the pit, or hell and torment—it was not the end. Consciousness continued. Once in, there was no way out; no escape from being, once one was made. The continuum stretched out into eternity on either side, whether infernal or beatific. Once born, one simply went on being and being and being. Thus, the extreme urgency of the chantries set up to serve souls otherwise beyond the reach of the church.

Paintings and instructive woodcuts of the medieval period show a devil and an angel on opposite sides of the deathbed, contending over the released soul of the dying. You *went* somewhere when you died then. In a didactic Lumière document of the Middle Ages, a disciple questions his teacher about the fate of even nail-parings and shorn hairs, so intensely minute was the interest in continued being. The teacher explains that all such off-scourings are not lost but constitute a kind of elemental compost heap out of which God will make a new person "without fault or excess, a hundred times more beautiful than the old." Pictorially, this same conservationist dogma is taught by the Torcello mosaic, which shows angels at work in a rather vigorous resurrection, not merely emptying graves but forcing a lion, an elephant, a bear, a leopard, a jackal, and a griffin to regurgitate the arms and legs of martyred anatomies.

We share at least this much with the Middle Ages, our secret fears about the body. Cancer patients these days have the same kinds of confusions about the me and not-me. For one's body to be eaten by a lion or a tumor is equally fearsome—the difference between us and them is that they took the continuation of creation seriously. Death transformed it, but death was never the end. Likewise for all cultures that made any of the provisions for the afterlife that we associate with primitivism. Little clay effigies, containers of food, tiny boats, furniture, weapons. Once in a while we hear of an expensive automobile being buried with its owner and are amused at such vestigial primitivism.

For a secular culture, death is something very different. It is not a journey, not a crossing, not translation. But the end. A blank screen. A void of imagining. Why, I wonder? A people only makes in its mind the things it desires. What is desirable about death as nothingness? Why did Hemingway, apart from self-indulgence, write "Our nada who art in nada"?

Self-despising is the only answer I can come up with. Erasure seems the only answer to our age's offended sensibilities. We can keep on living only because we have the promise that it will not go on forever. We can endure a bit longer only by believing that our execrable failure will one fine day be blotted out, erased from history, sucked up into some dark hole in the universe that eats, and then forgets, time. To think of this failed experiment we uncertainly call the human race going on forever, even in memory—even, or most especially, in the memory of God, the creator we have failed—is too painful to be borne. Better that it should be *as if* we had never been born. Such is the depth of our own self-despising. And that is why death as the end, the end of everything we have touched with our contaminated consciousness, is so sweetly desirable.

Well. This is not what I started to say. I see a few ducks and a muskrat and I start sounding like an overheated prophet.

The point is that the *refrigerium* is going to look so good that the more slothful among us are going to be hard to pry loose from our cozy beds in Abraham's bosom. Like butterflies that would go on sleeping eternally, unless their chrysalis cracked.

As I've already noted, light is the first sign of returning life. The sun comes in through our cabin window now at a quarter to eight and doesn't leave again till four. It seems amazing to be blessed with this much light now. And not just any light, but the stronger, more substantial light of spring. This is not an emotional delusion. A square mile of sunshine, compacted to fit like an egg in the hand, would have actual heft and weight—three pounds, in fact. Not a negligible quantity.

The second sign, after light, is water. Just as in Genesis. A good bit of the creek is thawed now. Although the snowpack on the high peaks has not yet begun to melt and descend the streams, the moisture in the meadows is turning from ice crystal to liquefaction. Or as they say around here, the frost is coming out of the ground.

I even bumped into a cloud of gnats today. The birds are going crazy over these sudden delicacies.

Two letters in the mail. Another divorce. And a nervous breakdown. What's wrong with you people out there? Is the world coming apart? Is the world disintegrating like ice floes like a thawing lake? When we leave here, will we have to jump from chunk to chunk, taking care not to fall through the cracks?

There seems to be no way, absolutely no way, unless one stops up every crack through which information seeps from the outside world, of avoiding these startling infiltrations of pain. Fatal knowledge leaches through the mails. Having friends exposes one to infection. Everyone seems to be living a non-stop disaster movie.

Death, it seems to me, would solve a lot of people's problems. In fact, this was affirmed as one of the functions of death by several of the early church fathers. Nothing that comes from God's hand is without grace. Not even death. If nothing else, it provides an escape from sin. Irenaeus says that God in his wisdom set a bound to what would otherwise be an interminable cycle of sin "by interposing death, and thus causing sin to cease, putting an end to it by the dissolution of the flesh, which should take place in the earth, so that man, ceasing at length to live in sin, and dying to it, might live to God." Certainly, if one had nothing to look forward to but an endless rerun of betrayal, deceit, and despair, death would be a welcome relief. Perhaps if we had a stronger sense of sin as itself the death of hope and of ourselves as animated corpses, we would not be so reluctant to accept the death of the body.

Cyprian, the African saint who was bishop of Carthage a century and a half before Augustine, and who, during his ten years' tenure had two major persecutions and a plague to contend with, had a good deal to say about death and not all of it bad. "If the walls of your house were tottering from decay, if the roof above were shaking, if the house now worn out, now weary, were threatening imminent ruin with its framework collapsing through age, would you not leave with all speed?" he asks. "Behold, the world is tottering and collapsing and is bearing witness to its ruin, not now through age, but through the end of things; and you are not thanking God, you are not congratulating yourself that, rescued by an early departure, you are being freed from ruin and shipwrecks and threatening disasters!"

That's looking at the bright side, I'd say. The conditions of human existence are such that death, if nothing else, delivers us from inexorable deterioration, from a life of endless sinning. Sin's dominion is over. We don't even know how grateful to be that Eve, having tasted the tree of good and evil, nevertheless abstained from the tree of life, which would have made our agony immortal.

Poor friends, what can I possibly say to you of comfort? Be glad you're going to die? That it won't last forever? You won't thank me for that, yet it's the only truth I know to tell you. The bitterness will die. It will soak right into the soil along with the disengaging molecules of your jellied corpse. It is not eternal. Your self-despising will incinerate as surely as your flesh and float up and out over the crematorium as only air, disburdened of emotion.

Does this not give you joy? This blessing is yours because you are flesh, because the earth and all its lovely laws can claim you as its own, can transmute you like any muskrat or leaf mold into a more profitable state. Hamlet meant it as complaint that "imperious Caesar, dead and turned to clay, might stop a hole to keep the wind away." He should have been rejoicing.

The spiritual that says, "Soon I will be done-a-with the troubles of the world" makes the same point as Irenaeus and Cyprian. And if the troubles of the world are of our own making, so much the better.

There is, of course, a dilemma here. If death is an escape from sin, does that mean that life itself is evil? One very easily slides into an anti-incarnational heresy here. There are a number of variations on this theme, from the Manichees who despised the flesh and all created being to Eastern mystics who aspire to a fine state of separation from incarnated being. The Tibetan Book of the Dead, the Bardo Thödol, while containing some quite commonsensical instructions on how to help a person prepare for death, also tries to teach ways of avoiding reincarnation.

Now I must admit that, considering what I have already quoted from the church fathers, reincarnation would indeed seem a horror. A life of repetitive sinning is too terrible to contemplate if one is doomed to endless reruns. And it is precisely of this that the Bardo Thödol warns the soon-to-die. They should be wary of becoming ensnared in karmic illusions again. "Thou wilt see thine own home, the attendants, relatives and the corpse, and think, 'Now I am dead! What shall I do?' and being oppressed with intense sorrow, the thought will occur to thee, 'O what would I not give to possess a body!' And so thinking, thou wilt be wandering hither and thither seeking a body."

The line is easily crossed here between the desire to escape sin, failure, and futility, and the despising of created life. The Buddhist may look with equanimity at death; this is commendable. But he also looks with horror on birth, the embodying of the soul. Christians are not allowed that.

It was a birth that brought our salvation. Our flesh is not the source of our sinning. Get rid of our bodies and what you have is a gang of decarnated spirits named Legion whose capacity for destruction is all the greater because it cannot be restrained even by the limitations of the flesh.

St. Clement of Alexandria, a theologian and a philosopher, could afford to express his views about death in more measured images than Cyprian, the pastor harassed by plagues and persecution. "The body," Clement begins with philosopher's dispassion, "as one sent on a distant pilgrimage, uses inns and dwellings by the way. It has care of the things of the world, of the places where it stops; but it leaves its dwelling place and property without excessive emotion. Readily it follows Him who leads it away from life. By no means and on no occasion does it turn back, but gives thanks for its sojourn and blesses God for its departure, embracing the mansion that is in heaven."

In other words, "this world is not my home; I'm just a-passing through."

So here is another problem. If this world is indeed not my home, then what *is* it? Clement's composure at the prospect of leaving this "inn" almost makes our earthly life seem trivial, like an excursion into time or a slumming expedition to the lower regions of being. This is perfectly understandable in one who believed, as he did, in the pre-existence of the soul.

My suffering friends, unfortunately, do not see themselves on a terrestrial holiday. If such were the case, they have certainly lingered too long to be amused. If they could see their sufferings as united to Christ's, then perhaps they could say that "to die is gain." But right now they only die, one day after another, despising their tottering house but impotent to leave it. One cannot separate the gift of life from the gift of the cross.

Fourth Sunday in Lent

The lakes have turned to jade now, a green stone common to Wyoming. What veins of snow remain threaded across their surface are like the flaws in rocks.

When I shift to my knees at the communion rail it strikes me again how everything must be turned inside out to be saved. It was by the act of eating that the cosmos was lost to its purpose. *So she took some of the fruit and ate it.* A simple gesture, ordinary, everyday. No mushroom cloud, no invasion of space ships. Just reaching out, closing the fingers around the globe, lifting it to the mouth. How offhandedly, even nonchalantly, death entered the world.

And now, by the same act of eating, grace enters. I put out my hand and take my savior. I swallow, the epiglottis closing off the trachea automatically, just as Eve's did, while the wine slips down my throat. The tree of life, denied in Eden, given here, for the life of the world. If our mouths were once the door to death, now they must become the gate of grace.

St. John Chrysostom says, "Let us, then, come back from that table like lions breathing out fire, thus becoming terrifying to the Devil." Whereas we fell by eating, our freedom suddenly impotent and flaccid, we now rise, also by eating, to fight. Actually, a lion is about the last thing I ever feel like, but today, amazingly, I could laugh all the way back down the aisle.

Snow last night. Sudden and unexpected and a couple of inches. This only two days after I saw the first returning mountain bluebird and David watched an immature golden eagle hunting over the meadow. The white cover of snow is startling now, after we had grown used to the bare ground. It looks as though someone has played a trick. Prankster's snow.

Another skiff of snow last night. It fell like a fine dust this morning and eventually dissipated like the Cheshire cat's grin. When it gets warmer I will go out and look for ducks again.

Only a week of winter left now. We are beginning to wait actively, like Lazarus, still lying in the tomb, opening his eyes, wondering what in the world is happening, waiting for the voice he might only have dreamed he heard to come again, to reverberate within the walls of the sepulcher.

We wait along with the earth. We too sense a growing light, if only by feeling the increased photons penetrating the soil above us. The frost is coming out of the ground, and so must we very soon. To what, we do not know; we only sense. Like butterflies within their chitin walls, we notice a feeler begin to form here, a foot there, a probiscus in between. What for? We have no idea. Such is the nature of calling. That's how it is—a call. One doesn't get the instruction sheet till later, after the call has drawn you out of the grave. All Jesus said was "Lazarus, come forth!" We still don't know what Lazarus did in those intervening years between the grave and the grave. We are so incorrigibly utilitarian that we'd want to know what for. What purpose will this extraordinary resuscitation serve? We aren't told. Not about Lazarus and not about ourselves. Until you answer it, all you get is the call—*come forth.*

Do not imagine that I am particularly sanguine about going. I'm not even sure Lazarus was. The corpse who staggered out of the tomb, the tatters of his grave-clothes trailing after him, was probably as uncertain of what was expected of him as I am.

One thing is clear. We were in no condition to be brought forth from the tomb last fall. Just because we had a future didn't mean we were ready for it. That was not the season of resurrection but of death. We couldn't have gotten from there to here without winter.

Edwin Way Teale tells us that the season of frozen activity is not wasted time for life forms, but is essential to their fruitfulness. They require cold as certainly as they do warmth to sprout. "Seeds that lie in the frozen ground, that are coated with sleet and buried by snow, are thus the most favored of all. Bring those same seeds indoors, coddle them, keep them warm, protect them from wind and cold and snow, and they sprout less readily in the spring. The seeming punishment of winter is providing, in reality, invaluable aid." What is true of plant seeds is also true of certain insect larvae. The eggs of the Rocky Mountains locust, for example, will not hatch without having gone through extreme cold.

"Winter cold, the enemy of easy life," Teale goes on, "is not the enemy of all life." He echoes Shakespeare's Friar Lawrence in assessing the earth. "What is her burying grave, that is her womb." But lest we slip too easily into stoicism here and swagger as we stumble from the tomb, let me say that toughness is not the point either.

One dies simply because one cannot go on living. If you're a caterpillar, you die because the food supply dwindles. If you're a human, it's because the ground is cut from under you. You fall into your grave and lie there, frozen stiff, until the summons to come forth startles you to life again. It is not a matter of choosing the hard life over the easy life. It is not a matter of courage. It is simply a matter of dying when there's nothing left to do. And of staggering out of the cave when one is called forth. The seeds and insect eggs make no claim to courage when they submit to cold and darkness, nor should we thus embarrass the cosmos by making a virtue of our necessity.

Snow. And no joke this time. It has come down for two days now, just like the sudden storm in September. It's funny, these two big storms bracketing our stay here so symmetrically.

A thin skin of ice has formed on the top of the creek and Lily Pond again, like a cuticle or a secondary eyelid. Last evening one pair of goldeneyes still maneuvered together in the patch of clear water like a two-boat armada. Nothing else stirred, however. No rabbits, deer, mice. They were still lying low under cover from the storm.

Winter is not giving up its hold on the land in one single gesture that flings the world toward spring. Just as the earth dies by degrees, so it comes alive again gradually, with a good deal of backing and forthing, flexing, slow suspirations. What winter yields one day, it takes back the next, only gradually giving ground as the hemisphere tilts toward the sun.

If the trapper who has haunted this canyon all winter had known about this storm, he might not have collected his traps three weeks ago. I hear he has caught a total of forty-eight coyotes, thirteen foxes, three bobcats. Sixty-four fewer predators. And a correspondingly larger population this summer of rabbits, picketpins, prairie dogs, and mice. Whose side can you be on and be on the side of life?

My ornithologist friend who lives up the canyon tells of a time on the Farallon Islands off the coast of California when she watched a fighter plane fly low over the rookeries where hundreds of thousands of sea birds were nesting. There was a time lapse of several seconds before the sonic boom, dragging behind the plane, hit the island. At the explosive noise, a whole heavenful of sitting birds rose simultaneously, and thousands of eggs, dislodged from the rocks and cliffs, shifted and were lost. A massive bird abortion by one insouciant act.

We may, if we work ourselves up to it, call this kind of destruction wanton, willful. A man in a plane, a far less subtle aircraft than a single gull's wings, suddenly ravages the niche thousands of birds have established. And not for food, not for shelter, not for any reason at all.

I suppose, if one were indeed on the side of life, one could, under such circumstances, make a case for war. Who else is going to prey on man, now that the saber-toothed tiger is gone, now that we have endangered every other species capable of weeding us out, except man himself? Without war will there be any sea birds left at all? Where do you go to enlist on the side of life?

Animals besides humans kill other animals, across species lines, it's true. And not always reverentially or even from necessity. There are wanton killers among the beasts too. Weasels kill whatever gets in their way and isn't too big. Sharks too, if the mood takes them, slash out steaks from the sides of their still living victims with a certain exquisite sadism.

But there are examples from the other side of sensibility too. My friend also observed on the Farallon Islands an incident involving an elephant seal that had been attacked by sharks. It hauled itself with great difficulty from the ocean up onto the beach where its herd had congregated. Its sides were sheared off; it had lost flippers. It was obviously going to die. Several of the other seals gathered round it, nuzzling it gently for a farewell. After a while, it turned, heaved itself toward the water again, and swam out to sea.

A similar incident occurred during the same season

involving a Steller sea lion. My friend watched a cow give birth one day to a premature pup, born too soon to be able to suckle. The mother nuzzled it about, swaddled it in her flippers, performed all sorts of maneuvers to get the untimely child to nurse, but to no avail. After a while, when her efforts became obviously futile, even to herself, she took the infant carefully in her mouth, slipped through the aisle opened for her by the rest of the herd, and, holding the pup above the water, swam out to sea, carrying it to its burial.

This is the other side of Tennyson's "nature red in tooth and claw." Sharks may well kill for sport, as does man. But elephant seals, the planet's largest aquatic carnivore, also have certain ceremonials surrounding death. And the sea lion mother performed some death ritual with her lifeless pup. Death was in some sense recognized and shared among the members.

Is it because we too harbor both kinds of behaviors, the shark's and the sea lion's, that we are able to isolate such events from their background activity and identify them as behavior?

Whitman was simplistic when he wrote, "I wish I could turn and live like the animals." We already do. We overbreed like mice and we kill more than we need to eat, like weasels. So what's the difference? A cruising fighter pilot or a cruising shark? Why should one be immoral and the other merely instinctual? Where did we ever get the idea that life has precedence over death?

For some strange reason, every living creature seems to have that notion planted in it. The instinct to preserve one's own life, even if one is careless of that of others, is the power plant of this earth. A suicide, on his way home to take poison, will, without even consciously deciding, swerve out of the way to avoid running head-on into an oncoming truck. We are all, in some sense, already conscripted onto the side of life, at least our own if no one else's.

The conviction lurks, however, that the shark's savagery, the weasel's wanton killing, is exponentially multiplied in us. Whereas a shark simply slashes out at the nearest victim with whatever teeth it's got in its head, human civilization goes to a good deal of trouble to trap a coyote or buzz an island rookery. A man, toolless, would not be able to kill forty-eight coyotes. That takes millennia of technology and implicates all of human history.

All species, ours included, may have as a matter of
common grace the unquenchable desire to preserve its own
life or that of its species, but do we attribute the
extermination of certain species, possibly even our own, to
mere ignorance? If there is some code buried in genetic
matter for desiring life, is there also some dark cryptogram
for wishing death? Not just the necessary death that supplies
us all with food, but death eternal, death of all life?

The third day that the snow continues to fall. Maybe we
won't get out of this grave after all. The winding sheet in
which the world is being shrouded piles higher every day.
Every now and then the ridges loom out of the thick sky
and then are veiled again by another surge of snow.

The people down in the valley, where they have had
only a couple of inches so far, are glad of this. The hay
farmers see their irrigation ditches fat with run-off. The
cattlemen make sleek snow cows in their mind's eye. The
bighorn sheep and the deer, the rabbits and the mice are
going to have a lean week of it. The sheep will come down
again from the high meadows but they won't find the
pickings any better here than there. All their forage will be
buried until the weather warms up enough to melt the snow
or, more likely, the wind redistributes it.

Still, what is our winding sheet right now will become
life later on—for the human community in the valley, for
their domesticated animals, and for the wild ones here in
the canyon. Spring snow is a short-term water storage
method. Wyomingites, unless they've got sheared sheep out
on the range, love it.

Farmers and ranchers, those who husband the earth or
herd its cattle, must always have this stereoptical vision of
life and death. Life is their goal, whether the life of their
alfalfa crop or cattle herd—or is it? The life they so
carefully guard and nurture at some point must be harvested.
The blade must slice its swathe through the grass and the
flesh eventually.

The images of harvest we remember from the Bible are
apt to fill us with lip-smacking contentment. Gorged
cornucopias, full barns, a laden table. Come, ye thankful
people, come. Yet if we examine the texts more closely, we
may grow squeamish.

Isaiah likens the people rejoicing at harvest to warriors gloating over their divided plunder. Other prophets go further. The harvest they most often describe is a harvest of bodies. The harvest is the image of judgment. Jeremiah told Israel that the bodies of the dead would fall like cut grain behind the reaper. And Israel's enemies will suffer the same fate.

> The Daughter of Babylon is like a threshing-floor
>   at the time it is trampled;
> the time to harvest her will soon come.

Hosea warned that a harvest was also appointed for Judah, and Joel coined the famous phrase about the Lord trampling out the grapes of wrath. The prophets most often turn the harvest image inside out: the hunter becomes the hunted, the harvesters become the reaped.

Mark's small parable about the kingdom being like a man who sows the seed that sprouts and grows night and day, he knows not how, appeals both to my sloth and my sense of mystery. But what about the ending? "As soon as the grain is ripe, he puts in the sickle, because the harvest has come." Is this the prophet's judgment harvest? Is this reaper grim or sleek? What part does he play in the kingdom?

Matthew's harvest parable is more explicit: "The harvest is the end of the age, and the harvesters are angels."

Whatever else we may wonder about in these parables, however unsure we may be about how to cast the parts, one thing seems certain: it is we who are harvested.

John's gospel makes it clear that, as branches, even the best of us do not escape pruning: "Every branch that does bear fruit he trims clean so that it will be even more fruitful." The best we can hope for is to escape with our trunk intact, all our appendages lopped off.

Suppose you're the wheat and not the tares; suppose you escape the fire and are one of the sheaves brought into the barn. The sickle still will be laid to you; you shall be reaped.

I sometimes feel a fair amount of affinity with Tatian, one of the more obscure of the early church fathers. An Assyrian born sometime around A.D. 130, he was a pupil of Justin Martyr and compiled the Diatesseron, the standard text of the four gospels used by the church in its infancy. Not much else is known about Tatian, except that he too believed in starting with the worst possible case.

Also, for some now irrecoverable reason, he had conceived an abiding abhorrence for all things Greek. He took on as his literary and theological opponents the most renowned writers of his day—Irenaeus, Tertullian, Clement, and Origen. All of whom he found to be infected with questionable Hellenic notions.

Especially did he find the idea of the immortality of man odious. Immortality is a quality, he claimed not unreasonably, that properly belongs only to God. He was appalled by the Greekified Christians' attempts to stake out such a claim for themselves. This he took to be the height of Hellenized human arrogance. Like the ancient Hebrews, he believed that flesh is grass. It gets reaped. That is its proper nature. We go down to death and return to dust. That's that. Let's not have any pretensions about immortality among mere creatures.

About mortality he agrees on only one point with the other church fathers. Death is the gift of a benevolent Creator. The end of existence, oblivion, may be terrifying to contemplate, but infinitely worse is the prospect of living on and on without God. In that respect, Tatian's mortality strikes me as more merciful than the immortality of the unredeemed posited by his colleagues.

Tatian found particularly distasteful Clement's Platonic idea of the pre-existence of the soul. This before-and-after-life diminishes the significance of life here on earth, our creaturely life-in-time. It makes of earthly existence either a mere excursion to the underworld or else only a preparation for bigger and better things, instead of the unique and unrepeatable event that it is, a drama fraught with real life-and-death choices. The promise of immortality discounts death itself, turns it into a quick ferry trip, as the Greeks pictured it, to the "other side."

But no, Tatian argued. Death is death. The end. Finis. Over. Give up these pretensions of slipping into something more spiritual when you die. You rot and that's that. You have absolutely no hold on God. You have no right to go on hanging around in any form whatsoever when your stay is up. Have the grace to go quietly. This is the state in which

Christians should live. Not imagining they have God in some theoretical hammerlock, not dreaming that they share as their due the realm of immortality.

Tatian believed in life eternal, not immortality. Life eternal does not mean going to heaven to live after you've vacated life on earth. Rather, it is being alive in God, now and always. It is not afterlife. If it is at all, it is now-life. It is no reward either for behavior or belief; it does not bind God in any way. The Vine does not promise the branches a spiritual retirement plan. They only have life as they continue in him, sharing his life.

Our life in Christ is not as a refurbished, more spiritualized model of our present selves. In Christ we are a wholly new creation. Just as God originally created man, so he has the power to bring him forth as a new creation. God does not recycle; he makes new. Or as Jaroslav Pelikan has interpreted Tatian: "God is able to call a man into actuality out of the potentiality that he alone sees. . . . The only man to whom God grants life eternal is the man who refuses to grasp for immortality on his own. God brings men not from life to death to life with smoothness and ease, but from life to death to life with the pain of childbirth and the pangs of death and the threat of nonexistence hanging over them."

If I have learned anything in this rocky tomb this winter, it is to take Tatian seriously. Death is real. We are all harvested—grass, grain, or tares. It is God's business to bring to life the seed that falls into the ground and dies.

Fifth Sunday in Lent

When we get up, the sky has finally cleared and the thermometer is down to zero. The last day of winter.

We feel our insides churning with uncertainty. Is this the way the insides of butterflies feel when the homogenous mush inside the chrysalis begins to coalesce into its first tentative form? If so, then birth is just as painful as death.

In addition to the regular Episcopalian calisthenics, we spend a good bit of our discretionary time in church this morning on our knees. The posture is a comforting one. Instead of having to sit up straight, holding oneself upright, you get to lean on the back of the pew in front of you. I find this exceedingly restful, both physically and spiritually. Kneeling is an outward and visible sign of my inner, invisible state of dependency.

After church we go to visit an old man who will be eighty-four next week. He first came to Wyoming when he was sixteen, a runaway who wanted to be a cowboy. He got to be a cowboy, a homesteader, and a hunting guide. He also got to go eventually to the Chicago Art Institute on the personal recommendation of Louis Agassiz Fuertes, the famous wildlife artist who happened to visit the dude ranch where the young guide was working. The cowboy ended up being a sculptor. A bronze casting of three bighorn rams sits on the table where he and his wife are eating lunch. The casting has an old envelope stuck to it with the purchaser's name written on it.

The Wyoming he remembers was even wilder and more rugged than it is today. The couple's only child died as an infant up in a mountain cabin inaccessible to a doctor. Some people would hold that kind of thing against a country, but not them. Their whole lives have been devoted to learning it intimately.

At eighty-four he looks mighty wintry himself. He's had three hips and two knees installed. He was scheduled to get new lenses implanted in his eyes this fall, but the doctor said they wouldn't take. His temper has degenerated somewhat since then. His world is going and he knows it. He has invested so much of himself into Wyoming that each new dam or diversion project is like blocking his own blood flow, each new cut for a logging road is a slash across his own flesh.

Never again will the world be the way he remembers it. It will never even be the way we will remember it when we leave here in only ten more days. Already the Forest Service has its stakes out for a new road up to our trail head. I am only half as old as Joe Back, but already I feel the press of time upon me.

At night I go walking down to the creek, crunching through the snow under a waxing moon that has turned the night to silver. The stars tremble in the sky like pendant tears. The water birches lift their bare tracery of branches against the blue, like feathers. I listen to the water running over the round stones. It will never be this way again.

I say good-by to winter.

First day of spring

Again zero this morning. A strange start for spring, perhaps. But when I go out to explore in the strong light of the vernal equinox, I find the farewell presents that winter has left us. On each pine needle, each leaf, each dry stalk of grass sticking above the snow are ice-leaves. Conglomerates of perfect and enormous crystals that cling to their base just like leaves. I stand under a limberpine as it dislodges a whole spray of these. They spin to the ground like thin chips of quartz, the falling leaves of winter. A sudden compression of all seasons in one moment. Here, on this day, the planet is balanced between darkness and light, the day and night of equal length. Death and life, not struggling for the upper hand today it seems, but meeting here, at this point.

I must admit this stereoptical vision of life and death makes me uneasy. I know about the necessity of the darkness for perceiving the light. I am familiar with the yin-yang symbol and Jungian psychology. I know the Fall was in some sense fortunate as there would have been no Incarnation and no Resurrection without it. I know we push God to ever more creative work by our own destructive tendencies. If Christ is the Life of the world, it is only by dying for the world.

Death is necessary. But it has in itself no making power. It cannot be the goal, as life is. It has tremendous gravitational pull; like cosmic black holes, it attracts its opposite, life, and devours it. Yet created life demands this opposing pole as surely as protons constitutionally demand neutrons. Like the black holes pulling in light, death pulls in life. It can pull, but it cannot push. All its power is centripetal. It cannot fling stars or planets, force roots through rocks, push babies through birth canals.

Even now, in this first day of spring, even with the snow piled up outside and a skin of ice over the pond so that the ducks have dropped further down the valley, even so, I feel, as I open my eyes on the light, a certain excitement. I recognize already the spring thrill, carried along on the bloodstream as surely as adrenalin. Our light receptors are triggered and the next thing we know we are giddy with eagerness.

So we don't know where we're going or what we'll be

doing one month from now. So what? We're being pushed
from between the rock walls of the canyon like newborns
down the birth canal. A certain amount of pain accompanies
the experience, but once we are delivered, the whole world
lies before us to be discovered with new eyes. Lazarus, you
will recall, did not roll over and pull the shroud up over his
ears when Life called him to come forth. And neither will
we. We may stumble some, and blink, but then we will go
on to the next episode in our creation.

We will not, however, curse the darkness that has
harbored us these winter months. Falling into the ground,
succumbing to that gravitational pull of death, is not a bad
thing. In fact it is a necessary thing. When climbing a
ladder, one must loosen the grip on one rung to grasp the
rung ahead.

Loosening the grasp is never easy for our kind. We
come into this world with our fingers furled and only
slowly, by repeated practice, do we learn to open our hands.
It takes a good deal of dying to get us ready to live.
Sometimes we simply refuse. We'd rather harbor what little
life we have than die and scrape out a larger space for the
Spirit.

But dying is what our life here on earth is all about.
Continually, daily, year after year.

There will be more deaths for us after this. This one
has simply been documented on the pages of the seasons. I
have been an apprentice of death, watching the way the
world dies.

Next time, when I must once again fall into the ground,
loosen my grasp upon my life, my plans, my self, perhaps it
will be with more skill.

In the afternoon we walk back from Trail Lake as the
sun is dropping over Whiskey Mountain. Again there are
sundogs cupped in the air on each side of the sun, glinting
off the suspended ice crystals high up.

Look, I say suddenly. Two eagles spiral left of the sun,
moving in and out of the prismed light precisely. The
sundog serves as their axis. They keep an exact distance
between them as they wheel on this hub of light. In some
austere eagle dance they shift their wings slightly on the
currents and ascend on a curtain of ice and light. Severe
and remote in their elegance. They two.

We two stand below gawking. Our hearts fly up after the eagles. We gulp for air at those altitudes. Oh, wait for us, we cry as they spiral higher and higher. Wait for us!

And then they are gone. Disappeared. Dissolved into an infinity of sky. *Such knowledge is too high. I cannot attain unto it.* They are embedded in air, have fallen upward into the sky. Two sown seeds. They are gone. The sun and its hounds are gone. The winter is gone.

Wind River Winter
was typeset on a Mergenthaler Linotron 202/N.
The text was set in 11 point Caledonia,
a face designed for the Mergenthaler Linotype Co.
in 1938 by W. A. Dwiggins.
This book was printed and bound by
Color House Graphics
of Grand Rapids, Michigan.